········ ESSENTIAL ········
New Age
PIANO EXERCISES
EVERY PIANO PLAYER SHOULD KNOW

Learn how to arrange and compose New Age music of your own!

Learn new age basics, including left hand new age patterns, chord progressions, how to arrange, improvise, and compose in a new age style, and learn original new age compositions for intermediate level piano students.

MUSIC MENTOR

JERALD SIMON

Music Motivation®
musicmotivation.com

Cool music that excites, entertains, and educates!

Music Motivation® books are designed to provide students with music instruction that will enable them to improve and increase their successes in the field of music. It is also intended to enhance appreciation and understanding of various styles of music from classical to jazz, blues, rock, popular, new age, hymns, and more. The author and publisher disclaim any liability or accountability for the misuse of this material as it was intended by the author.

MW00805627

I hope you enjoy **"Essential New Age Piano Exercises."** With this book, I hope piano teachers and piano students learn what I feel are the essential new age piano exercises that everyone who plays new age or contemporary classical music should know and be able to do well. I don't want teachers and students to simply read the notes on the page. I would like everyone who plays these exercises to know them inside and out. There are quite a few additional books in this series - and more to come. If you like this book, please look at my other books: **"Essential Piano Exercises Every Piano Player Should Know," "Essential Jazz Piano Exercises Every Piano Player Should Know," "100 Left Hand Patterns Every Piano Player Should Know,"** and **"100 Chord Progressions Every Piano Player Should Know."** I hope you enjoy these various books! You can learn more at **http://essentialpianoexercises.com**. Join the course today!

Your Music Mentor, Jerald Simon

This book is dedicated to my many piano students, young and old, who have asked me over the years to put together a book with all of the piano exercises I feel are essential to help pianists play better in all keys and in all inversions. It is for the many piano students enrolled in my Essential Piano Exercises Course (http://essentialpianoexercises.com). I create these books from this series for all of you!

Also, for my wife, Suzanne (Zanny), my daughter, Summer, and my sons, Preston and Matthew.

CONNECT with Jerald

http://musicmotivation.com/jeraldsimon
https://facebook.com/jeraldsimon
http://youtube.com/jeraldsimon
http://linkedin.com/in/jeraldsimon
http://pinterest.com/jeraldsimon
https://twitter.com/jeraldsimon
http://cdbaby.com/artist/jeraldsimon
http://instagram.com/jeraldsimon
jeraldsimon@musicmotivation.com

CONTACT Music Motivation®

Music Motivation®
Cool music that excites, entertains, and educates!
Music Motivation®
P.O. Box 1000
Kaysville, UT 84037-1000
http://musicmotivation.com
https://facebook.com/musicmotivation
https://twitter.com/musicmotivation
info@musicmotivation.com

First Printing 2021 - Originally created from 2006-2021 - Printed in the United States of America - 10 9 8 7 6 5 4 3 2 - Simon, Jerald - Music Motivation®
Essential Piano Exercises - $25.95 US/ $27.95 Canada - Paperback book - ISBN-13:978-1-948274-15-9 ; Music Motivation Cataloging: MM00001068

Music Motivation® is a registered ® trademark

Welcome to "ESSENTIAL NEW AGE PIANO EXERCISES" by JERALD SIMON

In order to better help piano teachers, piano students, and parents of piano students effectively learn music theory and what to do with that knowledge, thus bridging the gap between learning the scales and chords and using them to enhance music and make music of your own, I have created a course featuring step-by-step piano lesson videos to accompany this book: **"Essential New Age Piano Exercises."** You can visit ESSENTIALPIANOEXERCISES.COM to learn more about this course and gain access to hundreds of videos where I demonstrate how to play these exercises and many others, and then teach what you can do with them. Learning the theory is good, but knowing what to do with it is the practical application where I demonstrate how to use music theory to arrange, to improvise, to compose, and to create music of your own. More important than simply learning the theory is the practical application of *why* we are learning these scales and chords, and *what* we can do with them once we have learned them. It is the hands on approach to teaching music theory. In addition, I explain the theory in practical and simple terms so everyone can easily understand and know music theory for what it can do to help them in three primary ways: (1) sight-read piano music better and faster as a result of knowing the scales and chords, (2) take their music playing and music creating to the next level so they can improvise, arrange, and compose music of their own, and (3) ultimately feel comfortable and excited to learn music theory - the "FUN way!"

"My purpose and mission in life is to motivate myself and others through my music and writing, to help others find their purpose and mission in life, and to teach values that encourage everyone everywhere to do and be their best." - Jerald Simon

A message from Jerald to piano students and parents:

If you come to piano lessons each week and walk away only having learned about music notation, rhythm, and dots on a page, then I have failed as a Music Mentor. Life lessons are just as important, if not more important than music lessons. I would rather have you learn more about goal setting and achieving, character, dedication, and personal improvement. To have you learn to love music, appreciate it, and play it, is a wonderful byproduct you will have for the rest of your life - a talent that will enrich your life and the lives of others. To become a better musician is wonderful and important, but to become a better person is more important.

As a Music Mentor I want to mentor students to be the very best they can be. If you choose not to practice, you essentially choose not to improve. This is true in any area of life. Everyone has the same amount of time allotted to them. What you choose to do with your time, and where you spend your time, has little to do with the activities being done and more to do with the value attached to each activity.

I believe it's important to be well-rounded and have many diverse interests. I want students to enjoy music, to learn to be creative and understand how to express themselves musically - either by creating music of their own, or interpreting the music of others - by arranging and improvising well known music. In addition, I encourage students to play sports, dance, sing, draw, read, and develop all of their talents. I want them to be more than musicians, I want them to learn to become well-rounded individuals.

Above all, I want everyone to continually improve and do their best. I encourage everyone to set goals, dream big, and be the best they can be in whatever they choose to do. Life is full of wonderful choices. Choose the best out of life and learn as much as you can from everyone everywhere. I prefer being called a Music Mentor because I want to mentor others and help them to live their dreams.

Your life is your musical symphony. Make it a masterpiece!

The first book in this series is called **Essential Piano Exercises Every Piano Player Should Know.** This is the fourth book in the series. Other books in this series will soon be available as well (e.g. **Essential Pop Piano Exercises Every Piano Player Should Know, Essential Rock Piano Exercises Every Piano Player Should Know, 100 Chord Progressions Every Piano Player Should Know, 100 Improvised Licks Every Piano Player Should Know,** and so forth).

Most of the exercises in this book are written in the key of C, but I ask you to play every exercise in every key signature by moving up in half steps. I personally think you should be able to play anything by reading it in any key signature and also transpose or play something that is only written in one key signature to every other key signature.

It's funny because when I came out with my best-selling book, **"100 Left Hand Patterns Every Piano Player Should Know,"** I primarily wrote all of the left hand patterns and additional Fakebook songs contained within the FUN fake book section of the book (100 songs in Fakebook format) in the key of C Major. I did this intentionally because I wanted everyone to then transpose the left hand patterns and fake book songs into every other key signature. One of the main comments I received as feedback about the book was how so many piano players were having a difficult time transposing everything into every other key signature without having the music written out for them in every key.

When I came out with my next book, **"Essential Piano Exercises Every Piano Player Should Know,"** I decided to intentionally write out the exercises in every key signature. I wrote out and notated all intervals, scales, chords, chord progressions, etc., in every key signature so everything would be notated. I also did this because I added the fingering in every key signature which changes according to various key signatures. One of the main comments I received as feedback about that book was how so many piano players/piano teachers asked why I wrote everything out in every key signature and did not just write out the exercises in the key of C and ask them to transpose to other keys.

Most of this book, however, will be in the key of C Major and I will ask you to transpose and take every note up in half steps through every key signature. You can also transpose by following the circle of 5ths. We go over how to do this in the course which you can sign up for at <u>https://www.essentialpianoexercises.com/</u>. The Essential Piano Exercses Series teaches fun exercises through original music I have composed.

I believe piano players need to know how to read everything in every key signature, how to play from a lead sheet or fake book, how to play anything by ear, and transpose what they play from reading music to playing by ear in every key signature.

On pages 5 - 27, you will find the **"What Everyone Pianist Should Know" (Getting Started with the Piano - The Basics)**. This is a brief review of basic music theory concepts you should know as you start working on these exercises. This is a good review even if you are more familiar with everything. After that, the book introduces all of the original new age piano solos I have composed and the rest of the book teaches you what I feel are the essential new age piano basics every piano player should learn. The way I set up each of these Essential Piano Exercises books is to first teach you the theory concept, left hand pattern, or exercise. After presenting the theory, I demonstrate how to use it and even encourage you to create something of your own. I finally show you how I incorporate the pattern using an original piano solo.

MUSIC MENTOR

JERALD SIMON

The Music Motivation® Mentorship Map (for piano students)
by Music Mentor™ Jerald Simon

Music Motivation®
musicmotivation.com

	Apprentice (for 1st & 2nd year students)	Maestro (for 2nd - 4th year students)	Virtuoso (for 3rd year students and above)
Repertoire — In addition to the books listed to the right, students can sign up to receive the weekly "Cool Song" and "Cool Exercise" composed by Jerald Simon every week. Visit musicmotivation.com/annualsubscription to learn more and sign up!	**Music Motivation® Book(s)** — What Every Pianist Should Know (Free PDF); Essential Piano Exercises (section 1); Cool Songs for Cool Kids (pre-primer level); Cool Songs for Cool Kids (primer level); Cool Songs for Cool Kids (book 1); The Pentascale Pop Star (books 1 and 2). Songs in Pentascale position: Classical, Jazz, Blues, Popular, Students Choice, Personal Composition (in pentascale position - 5 note piano solo) etc.	**Music Motivation® Book(s)** — Essential Piano Exercises (section 2); An Introduction to Scales and Modes; Cool Songs for Cool Kids (book 2); Cool Songs for Cool Kids (book 3); Variations on Mary Had a Little Lamb; Twinkle Those Stars, Jazzed about Christmas, Jazzed about 4th of July. Baroque, Romantic, Classical, Jazz, Blues, Popular, New Age, Student's Choice, Personal Composition.	**Music Motivation® Book(s)** — Essential Piano Exercises (section 3); Cool Songs that ROCK! (books 1 & 2); Triumphant, Sea Fever, Sweet Melancholy, The Dawn of a New Age, Sweet Modality, Jazzed about Jazz, Jazzed about Classical Music, Jingle Those Bells, Cinematic Solos, Hymn Arranging. Baroque, Romantic, Classical, Jazz, Blues, Popular, New Age, Contemporary, Broadway Show Tunes, Standards, Student's Choice, Personal Composition
Music Terminology	Piano (*p*), Forte (*f*) Mezzo Piano (*mp*); Mezzo Forte (*mf*) Pianissimo (*pp*); Fortissimo (*ff*). *Music Motivation® 1st Year Terminology*	Tempo Markings; Dynamic Markings; Parts of the Piano; Styles and Genres of Music. *Music Motivation® 2nd Year Terminology*	Pocket Music Dictionary (2 - 3 years); Harvard Dictionary of Music (4 + years); Parts/History of the Piano; Music Composers (Weekly Biographies). *Music Motivation® 3rd Year Terminology*
Key Signatures	C, G, D, A, F, B♭, E♭ & A♭ (Major); A, E, B, F♯, D, G, C & F (Minor). Begin learning all major key signatures	Circle of 5ths/Circle of 4ths; All Major and Minor key signatures (Identify each key and name the sharps and flats)	Spiral of Fifths, Chord Progressions within Key Signatures. Modulating from one Key Signature to another.
Music Notation	Names and Positions of notes on the staff (both hands - Treble and Bass Clefs)	Names and Positions of notes above and below the staff (both hands)	History of Music Notation (the development of notation), Monks & Music, Gregorian Chants, Music changes over the years and how music has changed. Learn **Finale** and **Logic Pro** (notate your music)
Rhythms	Whole notes/rests (say it and play it - count out loud); Half notes/rests (say it and play it - count out loud); Quarter notes/rests (say it and play it - count out loud); Eighth notes/rests (say it and play it - count out loud)	Sixteenth notes/rests (say it and play it - count out loud); Thirty-second notes/rests (say it and play it - count out loud); Sixty-fourth notes/rests (say it and play it - count out loud)	One-hundred-twenty-eighth notes/rests. For more on rhythm, I recommend: "Rhythmic Training" by Robert Starer and "Logical Approach to Rhythmic Notation" (books 1 & 2) by Phil Perkins
Intervals	1st, 2nd, 3rd, 4th, 5th, 6th, 7th, 8th, and 9th intervals (key of C, G, D, F, B♭, and E♭). Harmonic and Melodic intervals (key of C, G, D, A, E, and B)	All Perfect, Major, Minor, Augmented, and Diminished intervals (in every key). All Harmonic and Melodic intervals. Explain the intervals used to create major, minor, diminished, and augmented chords?	9th, 11th, and 13th intervals. Analyze music (Hymns and Classical) to identify intervals used in each measure. Identify/Name intervals used in chords.
Scales	All Major Pentascales (5 finger scale); All Minor Pentascales (5 finger scale); All Diminished Pentascales (5 finger scale); C Major Scale (1 octave) A min. Scale (1 oct.); (Do, Re, Mi, Fa, Sol, La, Ti, Do) (solfege); All Major and Natural Minor Scales - 1 octave	All Major Scales (Every Key 1 - 2 octaves); All Minor Scales (Every Key 1 - 2 octaves) (natural, harmonic, and melodic minor scales); (Do, Di, Re, Ri, Mi, Fa, Fi, Sol, Si, La, Li, Ti, Do) (solfege - chromatic)	All Major Scales (Every Key 3 - 5 Octaves); All Minor Scales (Every Key 3 - 5 Octaves); All Blues Scales (major and minor); Cultural Scales (25 + scales)
Modes	Ionian/Aeolian (C/A, G/E, D/B, A/F♯)	All Modes (I, D, P, L, M, A, L) All keys	Modulating with the Modes (Dorian to Dorian)
Chords	All Major Chords, All Minor Chords, All Diminished Chords, C Sus 2, C Sus 4, C+ (Aug.), C 6th, C minor 6th, C 7th, C Maj. 7th, C minor Major 7th, A min., A Sus 2, A Sus 4,	All Major, Minor, Diminished, Augmented, Sus 2, Sus 4, Sixth, Minor Sixth, Dominant 7th and Major 7th Chords	Review All Chords from 1st and 2nd year experiences. All 7th, 9th, 11th, and 13th chords inversions and voicings.
Arpeggios	Same chords as above (1 - 2 octaves)	Same chords as above (3 - 4 octaves)	Same chords as above (4 + octaves)
Inversions	Same chords as above (1 - 2 octaves)	Same chords as above (3 - 4 octaves)	Same chords as above (4 + octaves)
Technique (Etudes)	Schmitt Preparatory Exercises, (Hanon)	Wieck, Hanon, Bach (well tempered clavier)	Bertini-Germer, Czerny, I. Philipp
Sight Reading	Key of C Major and G Major	Key of C, G, D, A, E, F, B♭, E♭, A♭, D♭	All Key Signatures, Hymns, Classical
Ear Training	Major versus Minor sounds (chords/intervals)	C, D, E, F, G, A, B, and intervals	Key Signatures and Chords, Play w/ IPod
Music History	The origins of the Piano Forte	Baroque, Classical, Jazz, Blues	Students choice - All genres, Composers
Improvisation	Mary Had a Little Lamb, Twinkle, Twinkle...	Blues Pentascale, Barrelhouse Blues	Classical, New Age, Jazz, Blues, etc. Play w/ IPod
Composition	5 note melody (both hands - key of C and G)	One - Two Page Song (include key change)	Lyrical, Classical, New Age, Jazz, etc.

This is only an outline or suggestion - add to it or subtract from it! If you are doing something different all together that works, keep doing it. This is meant to give you ideas and supplement what you're already doing.

The books from the Music Motivation® Series by Jerald Simon are not method books, and are not intentionally created to be used as such (although some piano teachers use them as such). Jerald simply creates fun, cool piano music to motivate piano students to play the piano and teach them music theory - the FUN way!

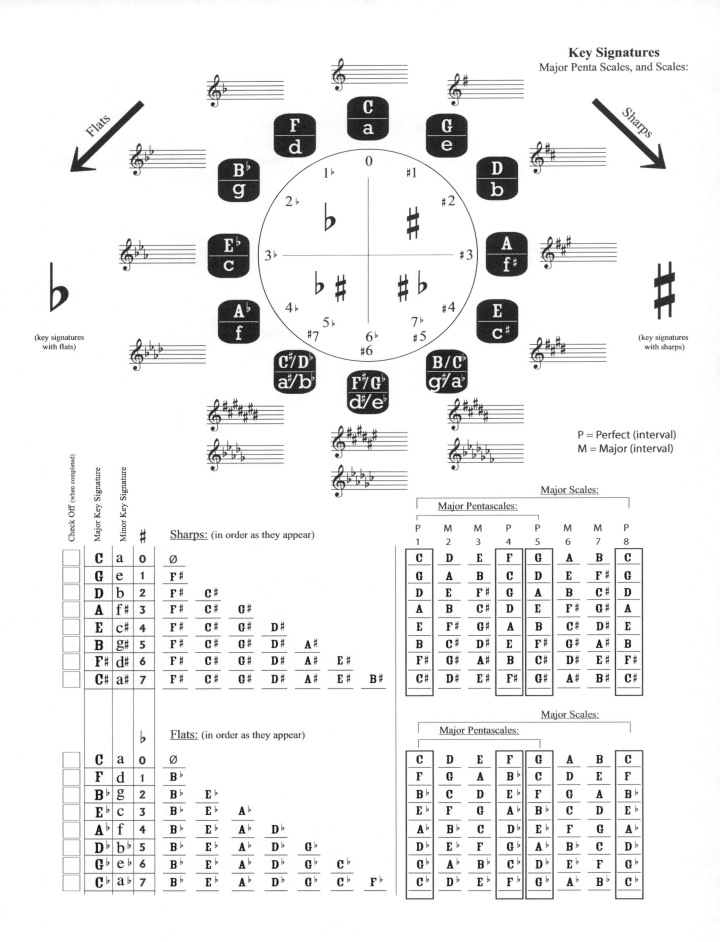

MM0000106

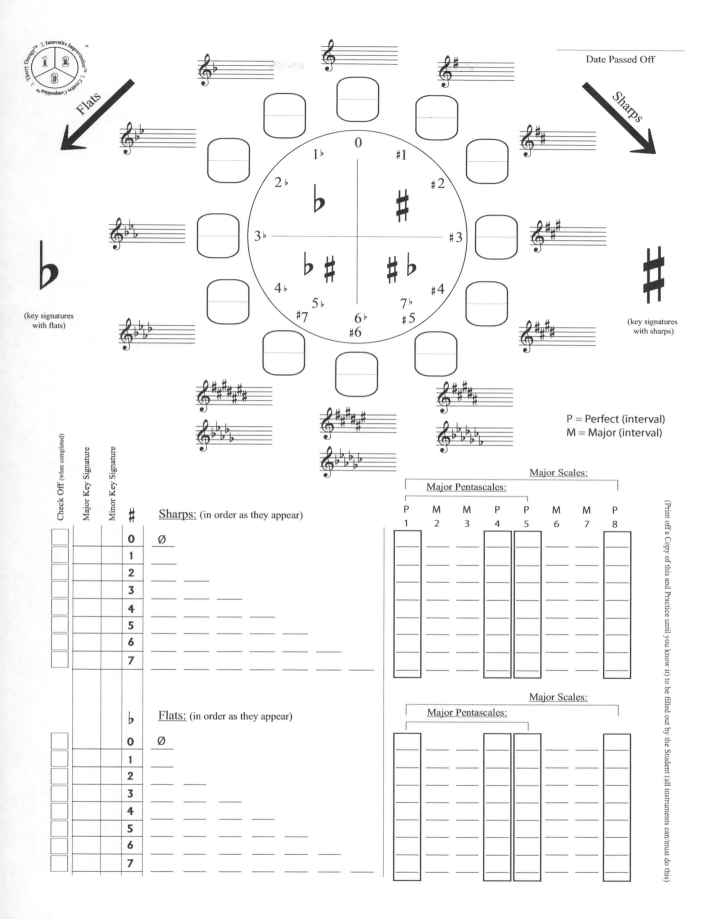

P = Perfect (interval)
M = Major (interval)

(key signatures with flats)

(key signatures with sharps)

This page has been left blank so you can make copies of this page to practice and test your knowledge of the Circle of 5ths.

All Major Key Signatures

(following the circle of 5ths)

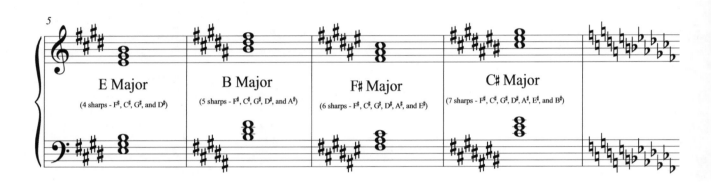

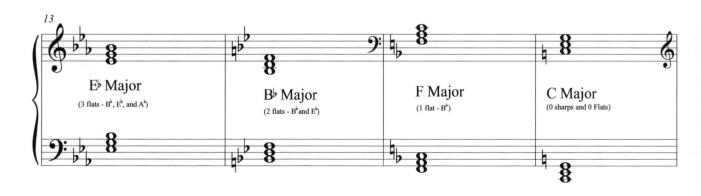

MM00001068

All Minor Key Signatures

(following the circle of 5ths)

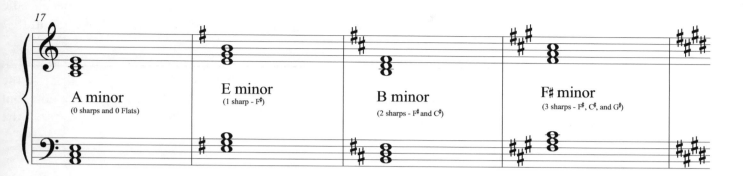

17

A minor
(0 sharps and 0 Flats)

E minor
(1 sharp - F♯)

B minor
(2 sharps - F♯ and C♯)

F♯ minor
(3 sharps - F♯, C♯, and G♯)

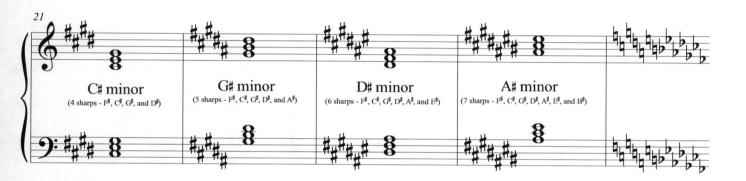

21

C♯ minor
(4 sharps - F♯, C♯, G♯, and D♯)

G♯ minor
(5 sharps - F♯, C♯, G♯, D♯, and A♯)

D♯ minor
(6 sharps - F♯, C♯, G♯, D♯, A♯, and E♯)

A♯ minor
(7 sharps - F♯, C♯, G♯, D♯, A♯, E♯, and B♯)

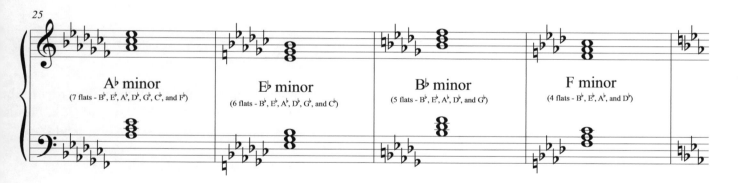

25

A♭ minor
(7 flats - B♭, E♭, A♭, D♭, G♭, C♭, and F♭)

E♭ minor
(6 flats - B♭, E♭, A♭, D♭, G♭, and C♭)

B♭ minor
(5 flats - B♭, E♭, A♭, D♭, and G♭)

F minor
(4 flats - B♭, E♭, A♭, and D♭)

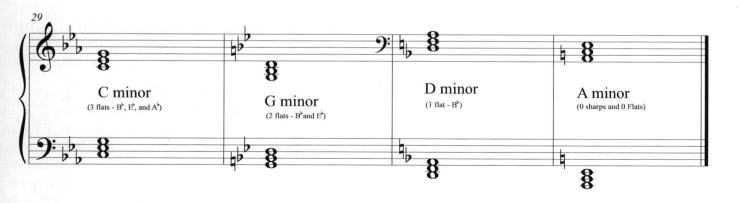

29

C minor
(3 flats - B♭, E♭, and A♭)

G minor
(2 flats - B♭ and E♭)

D minor
(1 flat - B♭)

A minor
(0 sharps and 0 Flats)

Let's talk about key signatures. You can refer to pages 8 - 11 as we talk about key signatures. When we talk about key signatures, the easiest way to explain them is by thinking about languages. Look at the chart of the circle of fifths on page 8 (a blank version is found on page 9). In the key of C major we have no sharps or flats. If we move to the right of the circle of fifths we will be in the key signature of G major. Think of this like learning to speak a second language. We have one sharp - F sharp (F♯) in the key signature. When we are playing a piece in the key of G major we will always have an F sharp (every time you see F, play F sharp {F♯} instead of F natural).

Any note in the musical alphabet (A, B, C, D, E, F, and G) can have a sharp sign (♯) or a flat sign (♭) placed in front of it. When this happens, the note either moves down half a step to the left for flats, or up half a step to the right for sharps. Let's look at the F note. The regular F note is the fourth above C. The F note is a white note, but when it has a sharp placed in front of it the note is taken up half a step to the right. The black note directly to the right of F is F sharp (F♯).

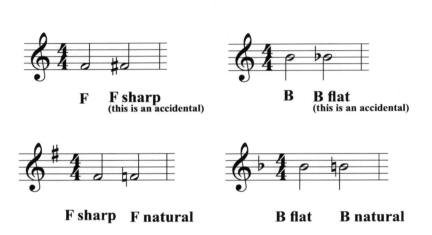

F   F sharp
(this is an accidental)

B   B flat
(this is an accidental)

F sharp   F natural

B flat   B natural

The first example to the left is in the key of C major. When the sharp symbol (♯) is added in the measure, you will play the sharp for that measure only. This is called an accidental note because it is not part of the key signature. After you finish playing the measure with the sharp, you will play the F natural again unless you see another accidental note. Below, the first example shows the key of G major (which has an F sharp in the key signature) followed by an F natural. The same examples are shown with B flat and B natural.

I like to have students memorize the order of the sharps introduced by saying this:

Five Cool Gorillas Dance And Eat Bannanas. Once they have memorized this saying, I tell them the order of the sharps is F♯, C♯, G♯, D♯, A♯, E♯ and B♯. For flats, I have them say: Better Exercise And Drink Good Cold Fluids. Once they have memorized this saying, I tell them the order of the flats as B♭, E♭, A♭, D♭, G♭, C♭, and F♭.

Memorize This! for key signatures with sharps   **Five Cool Gorillas Dance And Eat Bannanas**

Memorize This! for key signatures with flats   **Better Exercise And Drink Good Cold Fluids**

I like to have students first play all major pentascales in all keys following the circle of fifths. Aftery they can play all of the major pentascales in all keys, I then have them learn the minor and diminished pentascales in all keys. They can learn the patterns and the feel of playing the pentascales in all keys quickly. After doing so, they are then ready to play the major and minor scales 1 octave, then 2, and 3 octaves contrary motion (opposite directions starting on the same note - right hand goes up, left hand goes down), and parallel motion (both hands moving the same direction up and down the piano. I like to start with contrary motion because the fingering is the same for both hands and students learn the patterns quickly.

MM00001068

Rhythm Review (the basics)

Music is made up of notes (whole, half, quarter, eighth, 16th, 32nd, 64th, etc.) and rests (whole, half, quarter, eighth, 16th, 32nd, 64th, etc.). For now, we will introduce only the rhythms below. The whole note receives 4 beats (clap your hands once while counting to 4). The half note receives 2 beats (clap your hands twice while counting to 4 - clap once on 1 and once on 3). The quarter note receives 1 beat (clap your hands 4 times while counting to 4 - clap on 1, 2, 3, and 4. The eighth note receives 1/2 of a beat (clap your hands 8 times while counting 1 & 2 & 3 & 4 & - clap on everything. The 16th noth receives a fourth of a beat. Think 1 e & a which equals 1 & but now you will clap four times or play four 16th notes for every one quarter note. The rests mean you don't play anything for the same duration. I recommend the books "Rhythmic Training" by Robert Starer and "Logical Approach to Rhythmic Notation" (books 1 and 2) by Phil Perkins for a more in depth training in rhythm.

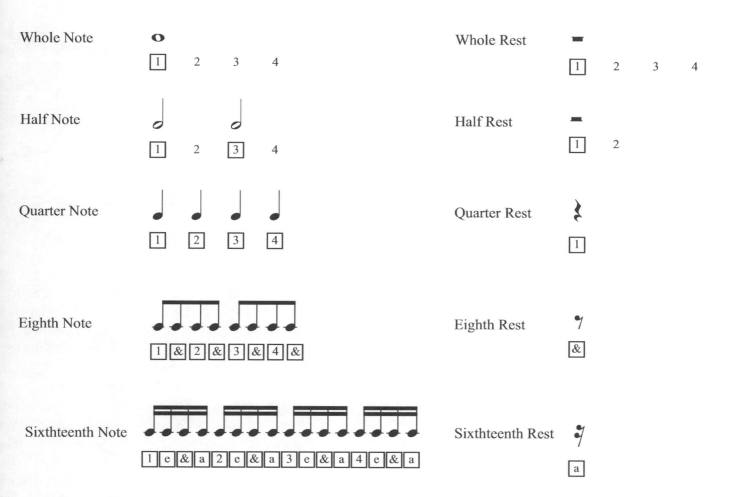

Try playing each of these rhythms on the piano. You can play these rhythms using A, B, C, D, E, F, or G. Try to play these rhythms on each of the black keys and all of the white keys. Try playing these rhythms using a simple C major chord (C E and G played together at the same time).

If you have a drum practice pad, try playing one of these notes with the left hand and a different note with the right hand. It's fun to play around with different rhythms.

♫ The Musical Alphabet ♫
A B C D E F and G

Learning music is similar to learning a foreign language. If you know your A B Cs, you already know the musical alphabet. The musical alphabet is A B C D E F and G. On the piano, the white note farthest to the left is A. That is the beginning of the musical alphabet. The white notes then continue as the alphabet does: A, B, C, D, E, F, and G. After G, it starts over again with A and continues up the piano (to the right).

The piano has a total of 88 keys. There are **52** white keys and **36** black keys. The note farthest to the left is A and the note farthest to the right is C. Here is what the **88** keys look like on a piano:

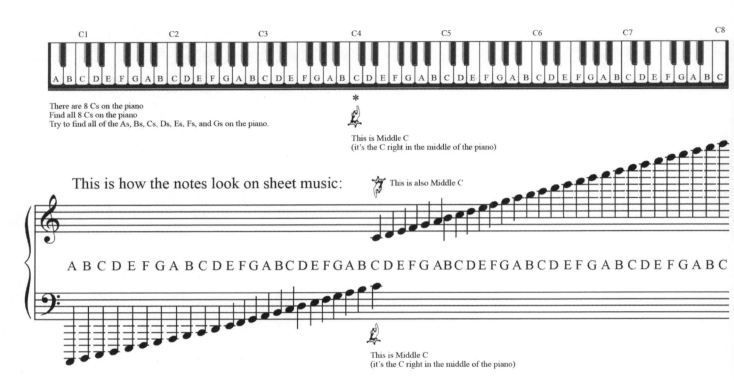

There are 8 Cs on the piano
Find all 8 Cs on the piano
Try to find all of the As, Bs, Cs, Ds, Es, Fs, and Gs on the piano.

This is Middle C
(it's the C right in the middle of the piano)

This is how the notes look on sheet music:

This is also Middle C

A B C D E F G A B C D E F G A B C D E F G A B C D E F G A B C D E F G A B C D E F G A B C D E F G A B C

This is Middle C
(it's the C right in the middle of the piano)

The first thing I have students do is play every note on the piano with one finger, starting with the lowest note "A" and continuing up to the highest note "C." I have students "Say it and Play it" - meaning they say the note name while they play the note (i.e. A, B, C, D, E, F, G, etc.). After they have done this, I have them find the pattern of 2 black notes together followed by 3 black notes together. I have students take two fingers with the left hand (the middle finger and the index finger) and play all of the 2 black note groups (both fingers play together at the same time) up and down the piano. Then I have students take three fingers with the right hand (the ring finger, the middle finger, and the index finger) and play all of the 3 black note groups (all three fingers play together at the same time) up and down the piano. After they have done this, students play with both hands (left hand plays the 2 black note groups and then the right hand plays the 3 black note groups) up and down the piano.

I then teach easy ways to find the musical notes according to these black note group patterns. All Cs are found to the left of the 2 black note groups (except for the last C - farthest to the right). Have the students find all of the Cs. All Fs are found to the left of the 3 black note groups. Have the students find all of the Fs. All E's are found to the right of the 2 black note groups. Have the students find all of the Es. All Bs are found to the right of the 3 black note groups. Have the students find all of the Bs. Once students have found these notes, I have them find all of the Cs on the piano and play (with either hand) C D E F G. This is the C major pentascale (5 note scale). Have students find all of the Cs on the piano and have them play C D E F G, first with the left hand and then with the right hand or vice versa. Students should be able to identify all of the notes on the piano and find all of the As, Bs, Cs, Ds, Es, Fs, and Gs on the piano. Make sure they can play the C pentascale (C D E F G) beginning on each of the Cs of the piano (except for the C farthest to the right, of course).

MM0000106

Now that you know the musical alphabet, let's see how the notes are written down so you can read and play music. Music is written on what is called a staff. One way to think of the staff is to compare the staff to your hand. There are five lines on the staff (this relates to the five fingers on your hand) and four spaces, one in between each line (because there is a space in between each finger). Here is what the music staff looks like - five lines with four spaces - one in between each line (hold your right hand horizontally in front of you).

The spaces on the music staff are numbered one through four counting from the bottom space (1) to the top space (4). The lines on the music staff are numbered one through five counting from the bottom line (1) to the top line (5). There are two principle staffs used in music when playing the piano (one for the right hand and one for the left hand). Each of these staffs has its own clef sign. Clef signs are symbols that organize a staff and help musicians know the order and position of the notes.

In piano, the two most common clef signs are the Treble Clef and the Bass Clef. The treble clef is also called the G clef because the second line (counting up from the bottom) is the G note and the treble clef wraps around the line. The top of the treble clef also wraps around the top space outside of the staff (which is also a G note). The bass clef is also called the F clef because the fourth line (counting from the bottom) is the F note and the two dots after the bass clef are on both sides of the line. This is what the treble and bass clefs look like. When you combine the treble and bass clef together (treble clef on top - played by the right hand and the bass clef on the bottom - primarily played by the left hand), it is called the Grand Staff.

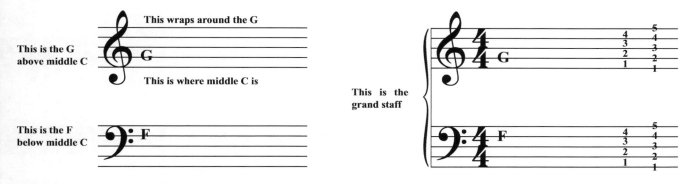

Music is written out by having notes, which look like circles or circles with lines on the side placed in the spaces or on the lines of either the bass or treble clef staffs. There is a different note (musical alphabet: A, B, C, D, E, F, or G) assigned to each space or line. Let's look at the notes of the grand staff (treble and bass clefs). We'll start with the bottom space of the bass clef. If you know your musical alphabet, it's pretty easy. The first space (on the bass clef) is A. The second line (on the bass clef) is B. It goes up alphabetically from there.

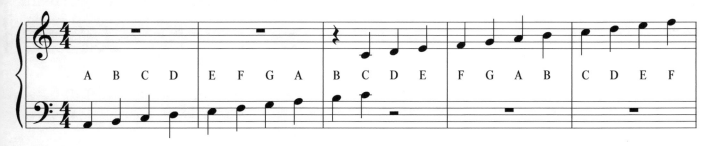

Watch your counting (M.M. ♩ = c. 120)

Have fun (Say it and Play it - count the rhythm out loud) play the right hand first, then the left hand, and then both hands together

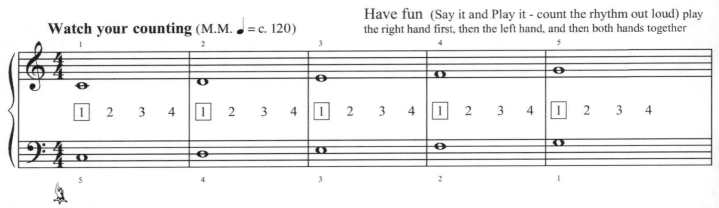

This is the time signature. This practice exercise is in 4/4 time signature. When you see this time signature at the beginning of the piece it means there are 4 beats per measure (clap and count to 4) The 4 on top means that there are 4 beats in each measure and the 4 on the bottom means that the quarter notes receive one beat. An easier way to explain this is by saying there are 4 quarter notes in every measure or something that equals 4 quarter notes.

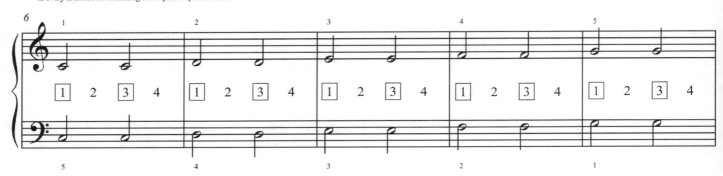

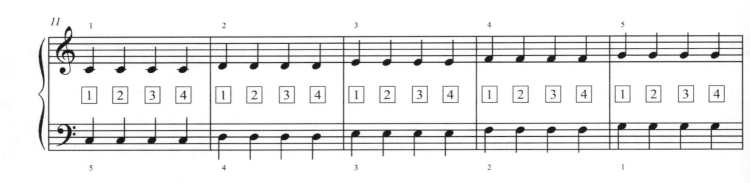

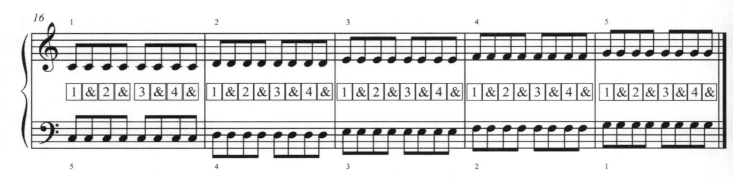

This exercise and some of the next few easy exercises are for beginning piano students and all of the exercises are taken from the Cool Songs for Cool Kids Primer level book by Jerald Simon ($14.95 - spiral bound book or $6.95 - PDF download of the book).

MM00001061

8va and 8vb

Not all 88 notes would fit on the bass and treble clef staffs alone. There are lines extending above and below the standard five lines of the staff. These lines are called ledger lines. The farther we go to the right, the higher the notes become and more ledger lines are needed. The farther we go to the left, the lower the notes become and once again, more ledger lines are needed. This is what all the white notes on the piano written in musical notation look like on the staff. Only the 52 notes represented by the white keys are shown here because the notes played on the black keys are the exact same notes as the ones shown below but there is either a sharp symbol (♯), or a flat symbol (♭) placed in front of them.

This is how the notes look on sheet music from the lowest A to the highest C on the piano (the first white key all the way to the left of the piano to the farthest white key all the way to the right on the piano).

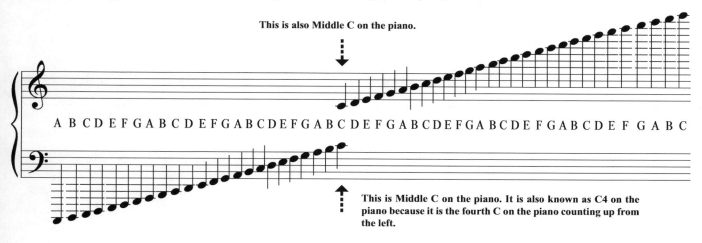

This is also Middle C on the piano.

A B C D E F G A B C D E F G A B C D E F G A B C D E F G A B C D E F G A B C D E F G A B C D E F G A B C

This is Middle C on the piano. It is also known as C4 on the piano because it is the fourth C on the piano counting up from the left.

The use of octaves (the same note eight notes above or below itself) was created to help the musician avoid having to count all of the little tiny lines above and below the staffs of the treble and bass clefs. The previous example is a little difficult to read because there are so many ledger lines. The octave sign (8va) makes reading the notes much easier because it removes several ledger lines. Below is an example of the same grand staff shown above but with the octave signs above (8va) and below (8vb) some of the highest and lowest notes on the piano.

This is how the same notes from above look on the sheet music with the 8va above and 8vb below the highest notes.

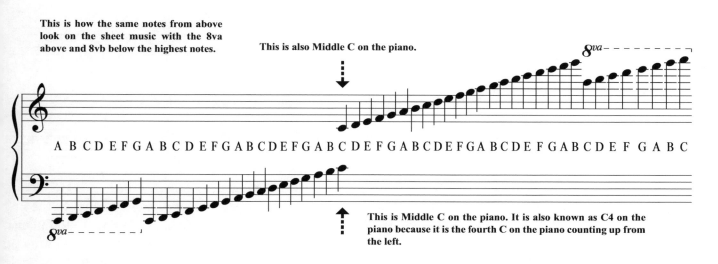

This is also Middle C on the piano.

A B C D E F G A B C D E F G A B C D E F G A B C D E F G A B C D E F G A B C D E F G A B C D E F G A B C

This is Middle C on the piano. It is also known as C4 on the piano because it is the fourth C on the piano counting up from the left.

With these simple building blocks of music theory, we can understand the basics of music.

Major scales are notes in alphabetical order. Let's take a closer look at the characteristics of a scale (we will use the C major scale for this example).

The individual notes of which each major scale is comprised, can also be thought of as degrees (1 2 3 4 5 6 7 8). The first degree is the tonic, the second degree is the super tonic, the third degree is the mediant, the fourth degree is the sub-dominant, the fifth degree is the dominant, the sixth degree is the sub-mediant, the seventh degree is the leading tone, and the eighth degree (which is the same as the first degree) is also called the tonic. These are additional names that can be given to any letter in a scale (such as C D E F G A B C, etc.), depending on its position in the scale. All of the notes in the musical alphabet can be arranged in different orders (which creates the various scales and modes - we talk about modes later in this book).

The tonic is always the first and last note of the major scale. It is also known as the key note because scales begin and end on it. The super tonic is the next note or second note to the right from the tonic (i.e. D is the second note to the right from the tonic C, so D is the super tonic in the key of C major). The mediant is the third note to the right from the tonic (i.e. E is the third note to the right from the tonic C, so E is the mediant in the key of C major). The sub-dominant is the fourth note to the right from the tonic, which can also be viewed as the fifth note below the tonic (i.e. F is the fourth note to the right from the tonic C so F is the sub-dominant in the key of C major). The dominant is the fifth note to the right from the tonic C (i.e. G is the fifth note to the right from the tonic C so G is the dominant in the key of C major). The sub mediant is the sixth note to the right from the tonic C, which can also be viewed as the third note below the tonic (i.e. A is the sixth note to the right from the tonic C so A is the sub mediant in the key of C major). The leading tone is the seventh note to the right from the tonic C, which can also be viewed as the second note below the tonic, (i.e. B is the seventh note to the right from the tonic C so B is the leading tone in the key of C major). This is what the C major scale looks like on music. Each degree name has been assigned to their corresponding notes. The degrees are shown with numbers and Roman numerals (which are often used when referring to chords - upper case Roman numerals mean the chord is a major chord, lower case Roman numerals mean the chord is a minor chord). Roman numerals can also have additional symbols added after them (a plus symbol {+} for augmented chords, a minus symbol { - } for minor chords, a raised circle { o } for diminshed chords, and a 6, 7, 9, 11, 13 after it identifying the chord as a sixth chord {6}, a seventh chord {7}, a ninth chord {9}, an eleventh chord {11}, or a thirteenth chord {13} - with any combination of the previous symbols).

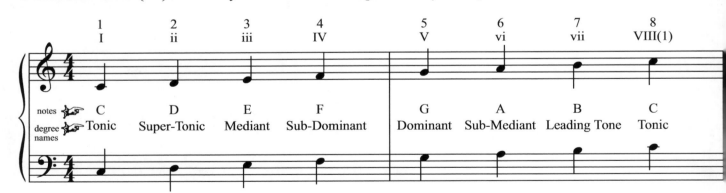

Memorize the degree names in order: (1) Tonic, (2) Super Tonic, (3) Mediant, (4) Sub-Dominant, (5) Dominant, (6) Sub-Mediant, (7) Leading Tone, and (8/1) Tonic. This is the same order of every key signature. In the key of C, the notes of the scale would be: (1) C (tonic), (2) D (super tonic), (3) E (mediant), (4) F (sub-dominant), (5) G (dominant), (6) A (sub-mediant), (7) B (leading tone), and (8/1) tonic. The key of G major has the same order but the note names of the degrees change, nothing else changes. In the key of G, the notes of the scale would be: (1) G (tonic), (2) A (super tonic), (3) B (mediant), (4) C (sub-dominant), (5) D (dominant), (6) E (sub-mediant), (7) F (leading tone), and (8/1) tonic. The degree names are the same!

MM00001068

Prime or Perfect First, Major Second, Major Third, Perfect Fourth, Perfect Fifth, Major Sixth, Major Seventh, Perfect Eighth (or octave)

Look at the example below - these are intervals. An interval is defined as the distance (comprised of whole and half steps) between two notes. The major scale uses "Perfect" and "Major" intervals. The perfect intervals are the primary notes (from which the primary chords are created) from the major scale (i.e. 1 or C; 4 or F: and 5 or G). The major intervals are the secondary notes (from which the secondary chords are created) from the major scale (i.e. 2 or D; 3 or E; 6 or A; and 7 or B). Look at the intervals of the C major scale below. Once you feel comfortable playing this exercise in the key of C, try playing it in every key moving up chromatically in half steps. I recommend playing every exercise and jazz piece in this book in every key!

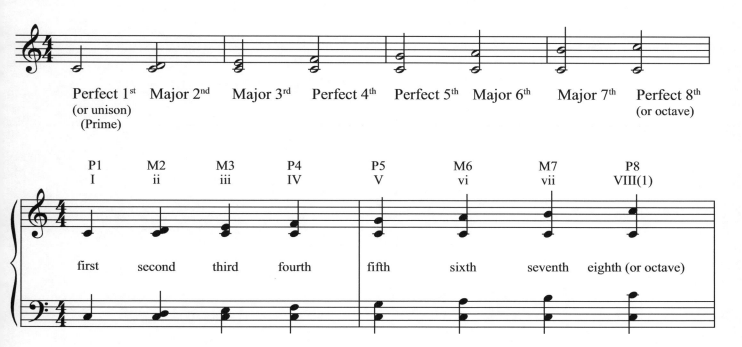

Perfect interior can become a diminished interval by playing the flat (i.e. C and G♭ is a diminished 5th interval) and an augmented interval by playing the sharp (i.e. C and G♯ is an augmented 5th interval). Major intervals can become a diminished interval by playing the double flat (C and B♭♭ is a diminished 7th interval), a minor interval by playing the flat (i.e. C and B♭ is a minor 7th interval), and an augmented interval by playing the sharp (i.e. C and B♯ is an augmented 7th interval).

When 2 or more intervals are stacked on top of each other, they are called blocked intervals. Blocked intervals are also called harmonic intervals (i.e. a harmonic major 3rd interval is C and E played together at the same time). When they are are placed next to each other (one after the other), they are called broken intervals (these are not stacked on top of each other and are not played at the same time. Broken intervals are also called melodic intervals (i.e. a melodic major 3rd interval is C and E played one after another).

Chords are created when two or more intervals (generally three) are stacked on top of each other. Some chords are major (happy sounding), some are minor (sad sounding), some are diminished (spooky and scary or deranged sounding), and there are many more. On the next page, I want you to play the triads (three note chords) created from stacking thirds on top of the notes from the C major scale. Notice the chord progression is Major - minor - minor - Major - Major - minor - diminished - Major. This is the same chord progression for all of the major scales. The corresponding Roman numerals are I - ii - iii - IV - V - vi - vii° - I.

On the next page I have included a simple and **"Quick Chord Chart"** to help you quickly begin to create the most common chords. In the chart below, I use the most common chords created from the notes of the C major scale (i.e. C Major, C minor, C diminished, etc.). Let me explain the chart on the next page.

On the left side, there is a column that says, "Most Common Chords," and has the chord name listed below (i.e. Major, Minor, Diminished, Augmented, etc.). This can be applied to all key signatures and you can do this for every key signature.

I use the key of C Major as an example. The next two columns show the chord symbols (i.e. C, Cm, Cº, C⁺, etc.). I have listed the short and long variations of the chords. They mean the same thing. The next columns are listed P1, m2, M2, m3, M3, P4, d5, P5, A5, M6/d7, m7, and M7. These abbreviations mean the following:

P1 = Perfect 1st interval (or Prime/Unison) (i.e. C)

m2 = minor 2nd interval (i.e. C - D flat)

M2 = major 2nd interval (i.e. C - D)

m3 = minor 3rd interval (i.e. C - E flat)

M3 = major 3rd interval (i.e. C - E)

P4 = Perfect 4th interval (i.e. C - F)

d5 = diminished 5th interval (i.e. C - G flat)

P5 = Perfect 5th interval (i.e. C - G)

A5 = augmented 5th interval (i.e. C - G sharp)

M6 = major 6th interval (i.e. C - A), or
d7 interval (i.e. C - B double flat which is an A)

m7 = minor 7th interval (i.e. C - B flat)

M7 = major 7th interval (i.e. C - B)

Try playing these intervals in all keys on the piano!

Memorize all of these intervals . This example shows C.

MM00001068

An interval is the distance from one note to another note. As an example, a major 2nd interval (M2) is from C to D.

Quick Chord Chart for reference purposes (use this to quickly identify how to create your chords)
In this example we demonstrate with chords created from the C Major Scale. You can do this for all keys!

Most Common Chords			Qualities and attributes of individual notes within the chord											
Chord Name (This applies to all keys)	**Chord Symbols** (I use C as an example)		Interval	P1	m2	M2	m3	M3	P4	d5	P5	A5	M6/d7	m7	M7
Notes from the C Major Scale	Short	Long		C	D♭	D	E♭	E	F	G♭	G	G♯	A or B♭♭	B♭	B
Major triad	C	Cmaj	P1					M3			P5				
Minor triad	Cm	Cmin	P1				m3				P5				
Diminished triad	C°	Cdim	P1				m3			d5					
Augmented triad	C⁺	Caug	P1					M3				A5			
Sus4 triad	Csus	Csus4	P1						P4		P5				
Sus2 triad	Csus2	Csus2	P1			M2					P5				
Major sixth chord (6th)	C6	Cmaj6	P1					M3			P5		M6		
Minor sixth chord (m6th)	Cm6	Cmin6	P1				m3				P5		M6		
Major seventh chord	CM7	Cmaj7	P1					M3			P5				M7
Minor-major seventh chord	CmM7	CminMaj7	P1				m3				P5				M7
Dominant seventh chord	C7	Cdom7	P1					M3			P5			m7	
Minor seventh chord	Cm7	Cmin7	P1				m3				P5			m7	
Minor seventh flat five chord	Cm7(-5)	Cmin7(-5)	P1				m3			d5				m7	
Minor seventh sharp five chord	Cm7(+5)	Cmin7(+5)	P1				m3					A5		m7	
Diminished seventh chord	C°⁷	Cdim7	P1				m3			d5			d7		
Augmented seventh chord	C⁺⁷	Caug7	P1					M3				A5		m7	

P = perfect interval (i.e. P4), **m** - minor interval (i.e. m2), **M** = major interval (i.e. M7), **d** = diminished interval (i.e. d5), **A** = augmented interval (i.e. A5)

Now try to create these same chords in every key signature on the piano - C, C♯, D, E♭, E, F, F♯, G, A♭, A, B♭, and B. It's a great exercise and something you should learn how to do if you don't already know. Sit down at the piano and play these in the key of C. After doing that, try to play all major scales on the piano in every key signature (I include all of the major scales and chords in my book, "Essential Piano Exercises Every Piano Player Should Know").

As a fun review, I would like you to play the most common chords in every key signature and read them printed out on the paper. These next few pages are taken from my book, "Essential Piano Exercises Every Piano Player Should Know." For those who have already purchased that book, this will be a review. For everyone else who has not yet purchased that book, I highly recommend purchasing it to learn what I personally feel are the basics every piano player should know (i.e. intervals, pentascales, major and minor scales, triad chords, 6th, 7th, chord progressions etc.). If you are a member of the Essential Piano Exercises course (essentialpianoexercises.com), you already have access to this book in PDF format.

With a good understanding of major and minor intervals, you can begin creating the basic triad chord (or three note chord). The three most common triad chords are the major chord, the minor chord, and the diminished chord. There are, of course, augmented chords, suspend the fourth chords, and suspend the second chords, but for now, we will only cover the major, minor, and diminished chords.

All major chords are created by combining the perfect 1st and 5th intervals (i.e C and G) with the major 3rd interval (i.e. E). With all three combined, the major triad chord is created (i.e. C, E, and G played together create the C major chord). All minor chords are created by combining the perfect 1st and 5th intervals (i.e. C and G) with the minor 3rd interval (i.e. E♭). With all three combined, the minor triad chord is created (i.e. C, E♭, and G played together create the C minor chord). All diminished chords are created by combining the perfect 1st interval (i.e. C) the diminished 5th interval (i.e. G♭) and the minor 3rd interval (i.e. E). With all three combined, the diminished triad chord is created (i.e. C, E♭, and G♭ played together create the C diminished chord).

Play the triads created from the C major scale below (each of the triads begin on one of the notes from the C major scale - moving up one octave - C, D, E, F, G, A, B, and ending with C).

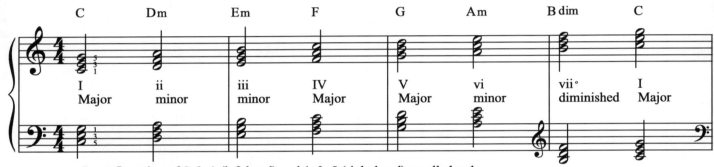

Same fingering of 5, 3, 1 (left hand) and 1, 3, 5 (right hand) on all chords

The chord progression of Major, minor, minor, Major, Major, minor, diminished, Major is the same in every key signature. Above the grand staff you will find the name of the chord(s). In the middle of the grand staff you will find the corresponding roman numeral. If the Roman numeral is upper case (i.e. I) it means the chord is major, and if the Roman numeral is lower case (i.e. i) it means the chord is minor. If the Roman numeral is lower case with the diminished symbol after it (i.e. i°) it means the chord is diminished. Since all I, IV, and V chords are always major chords (when created from the major scale) they are called the primary chords and used more frequently. The ii, iii, vi, and vii chords are called secondary chords because they are not major chords (they are minor chords and one diminished chord). Play the primary chords below for C major and A minor key signatures.

Primary chords for C Major

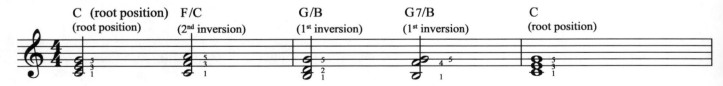

Primary chords for A minor

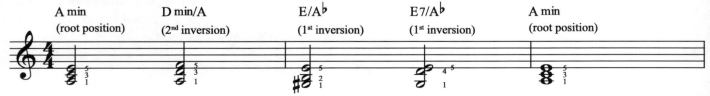

MM00001068

So far we have focused on the basics. For many of you, this has most likely been a review. That is intentional as we will use these basics as a foundation and build on what we have learned so far. On the next six pages, we will introduce the most common chords found in music. There are, of course, many more chords, but these are the most common chords used in every key signature. On this page, we will introduce a few simple left hand patterns you can use to begin to arrange music of your own. These are basic left hand patterns. All of these left hand patterns have been taken from my book, 100 Left Hand Patterns Every Piano Player Should Know. This is one of my best-selling music theory books and is also one of the books from the Essential Piano Exercises Series and course (https://www.essentialpianoexercises.com/).

Try these left hand patterns as they are written out and then try to play them in every key signatures moving up in half steps. It's a fun exercises and challenges the brain as well as the fingers.

This is a broken perfect 5th interval (melodic 5th) played as a whole, half, quarter, or eighth notes.

This is a blocked perfect 5th interval (harmonic 5th) played as whole, half, quarter, or eighth notes.

This is a C Major chord (triad - three note chord) that is blocked and played as whole, half, quarter, or eighth notes.

This is a C Major Chord (triad - three note chord) that is broken apart.

This is a variation of a broken C Major chord (quarter and eighth notes).

Most Common Chords (in all keys)

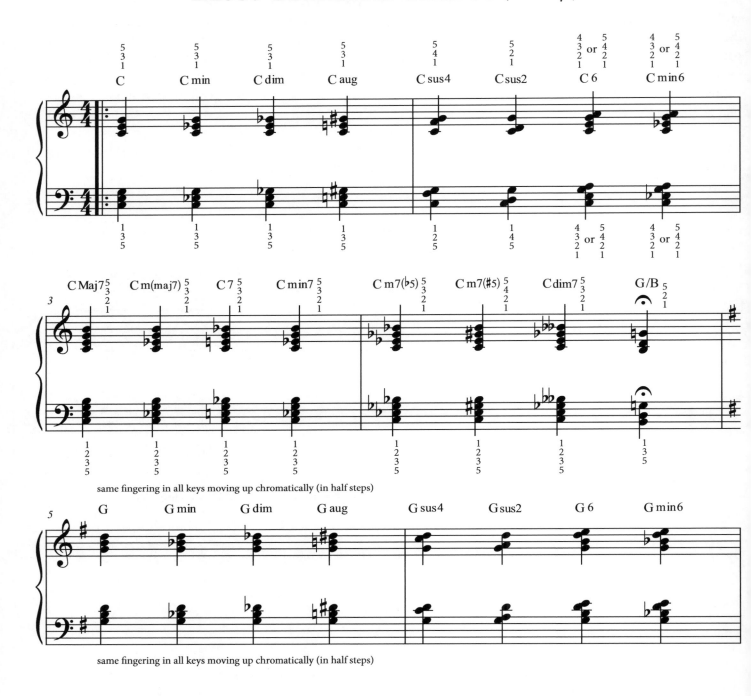

same fingering in all keys moving up chromatically (in half steps)

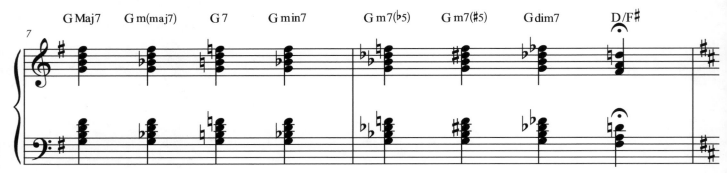

same fingering in all keys moving up chromatically (in half steps)

MM00001068

MM00001068

23

MM00001068

MM00001068

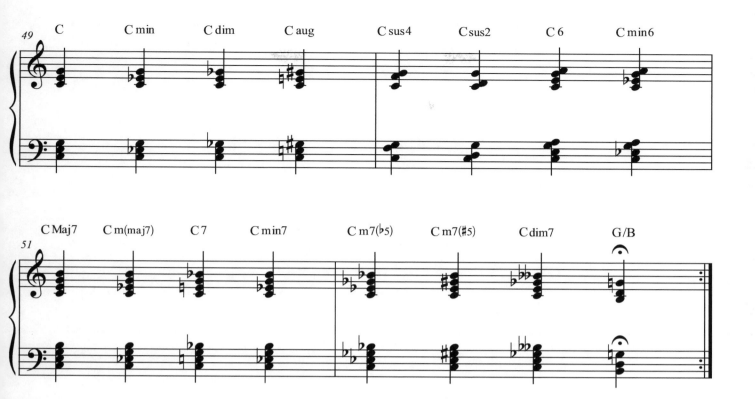

Now that you have played the most common and basic chords in every key signature in root position, I will ask you to play every one of the chords found on the previous six pages in every key signature and in every inversion as well. Every chord has a root position, (which is what you played on these pages), and additional positions called inversions. If a chord has three notes as is the case in a Major, Minor, Diminished, Augmented, Sus4 or Sus2 chord, then you will have three positions - root position, first inversion, and second inversion.

Let's take a C Major chord as an example. There are three notes in the C Major chord - C E G. When C is on the bottom and E and G are on top, it is called a C Major chord in root position (C E G - look at measure 49 of this page as an example of a C Major chord in root position). When the chord is inverted and the C is added to the top of the chord instead of the bottom (i.e. E G C - where E is on the bottom and C is on the top), this is called a C Major chord in first inversion. When the chord is inverted again and the E is on the top of the chord instead of the bottom (i.e. G C E - where G is on the bottom and E is on the top), this is called a C Major chord in second inversion. The same is true for the Major, Minor, Diminished, Augmented, Sus4 or Sus2 chord. Each of these chords has a root position, first inversion, and second inversion.

If a chord has four notes as is the case in the 6th, minor 6th, Major 7th, Minor Major 7th, Dominant 7th, Minor 7th, chord, then you will have four positions - root position, first inversion, second inversion, and third inversion.

In my book, "Essential Piano Exercises Every Piano Player Should Know," I wrote out all of the root positions and first, second, and third inversions in every key signature for all of the chords written above. If you have that book, you can play every chord in every key and in every inversion by reading what is written out in the sheet music. For those who don't have that book yet, simply take what I have written out above and play all of the most common chords in every key signature and in every inversion (root, first, second, and third inversions when playing the 6th or 7th chords). Before moving on in this book, play these chords in every key and in every inversion.

List of New Age Pieces in this book with the accompanying page number:

As mentioned earlier in this book, the entire format or outline of this book is to teach the music theory of a certain concept and demonstrate the practical application of that music theory in an exercise. After teaching you the theory and having you play the exercise, I often have you follow the progression or pattern and then you try to create or improvise a piece of your own. I then introduce a new age piece I have composed specifically following the music theory, intervals, scales, patterns, and exercises you have just learned. It's a fun way for you to learn these essential new age piano exercises and apply them yourself and then see how I applied them to the real world of music.

Essentially every original new age piano piece I have composed in this book, was created as an exercise - albeit a really fun exercise. You will see the left hand patterns you have learned from this book combined with intervals, chords, scales, and other musical new age patterns in each new age piece. Think of this book as fun exercises combined with fun new age piano solos which are, in and of themselves, additional exercises. As with previous Essential Piano Exercises books, once you feel comfortable playing these exercises in the key of C, try to play them in every key signature! Have fun with this book!

MM00001068

In this exercise, the left hand starts out playing a harmonic 5th perfect interval (refer back to the intervals explained on pages 17 and 18 of this book). After three measures, the left hand begins playing the melodic 5th interval. The right hand starts off playing harmonic 3rd intervals and then uses notes from the C Major pentascale (i.e. C D E F and G), in various rhythms and sequences. The first three lines primarily follow a pattern of starting on the Tonic (i.e. C) and moving to the Super Tonic (i.e. D). Starting in measure 15, we follow a chord progression of I - vi - IV - V (i.e. C Major - A minor - F Major - G Major. Have fun playing this fun chord progression.

In this exercise, we are playing all broken 5th inverals with the left hand moving up according to the C Major scale (i.e. C D E F G A B C). The right hand is playing a simple pattern created from the pentascale starting on C, D, E, F, G, A, B, and C.

You can play this pattern freely and with feeling. Most of the exercises in this book do not have any dynamic markings on purpose so you can play them however you feel you should. The new age pieces I have composed throughout this book do have dynamic markings because that is how they were recorded on the albums - but you can play the music how you think it should sound. For fun, try to play this example in every key signature on the piano - C, C♯, D, E♭, E, F, F♯, G, A♭, A, B♭, and B.

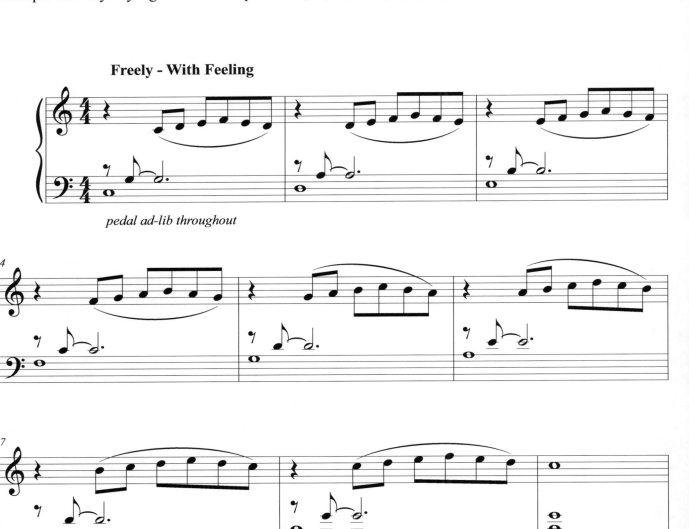

MM00001068

In this exercise, we are creating a simple New Age sounding piece using broken 5th intervals with the left hand and the notes from the C Major pentascale (i.e. C D E F and G) with the right hand. For fun, try to play this example in every key signature on the piano - C, C♯, D, E♭, E, F, F♯, G, A♭, A, B♭, and B.

Freely - With Feeling

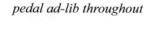

pedal ad-lib throughout

In this exercise, we are playing all blocked and broken 3rd inverals (i.e. C and E) moving up according to the C Major scale (i.e. C D E F G A B C). After playing the third intervals, we invert the interval. Essentially, we take the bottom note and move it to the top. So the third interval of C and E, for example, become E and C where C is on the top. This is known as a 6th interval. All third intervals when inverted become 6th intervals. Try playing this exercise. For fun, try to play this example in every key signature on the piano - C, C♯, D, E♭, E, F, F♯, G, A♭, A, B♭, and B.

MM00001068

Here is a very simple melody I composed to teach you how to take the notes C D E F G A and B and create a simple melodic line with the right hand. First play the melody as it is written. The left hand is very simple - one note - and that is intentional.

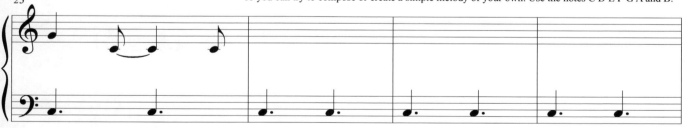

Now, for fun, try to create a simple melody of your own. The right hand has been left blank on purpose so you can try to compose or create a simple melody of your own. Use the notes C D E F G A and B.

In the piece below, I wanted to create a simple new age sounding piece that used a perfect fifth interval with the left hand while the right hand plays notes from the C Major pentascale (C D E F and G). Later in the piece, you will notice we are primarily using blocked third intervals (starting in measure 17), and then using blocked sixth intervals (starting in measure 21). Try it!

NEW WORLD ADVENTURE

BY JERALD SIMON

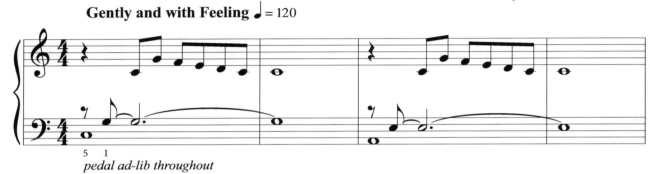

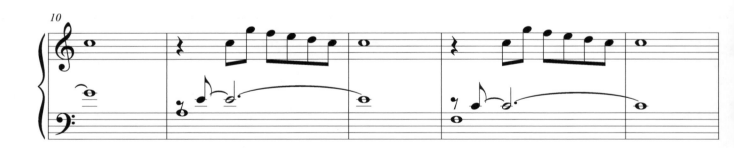

MM00001068

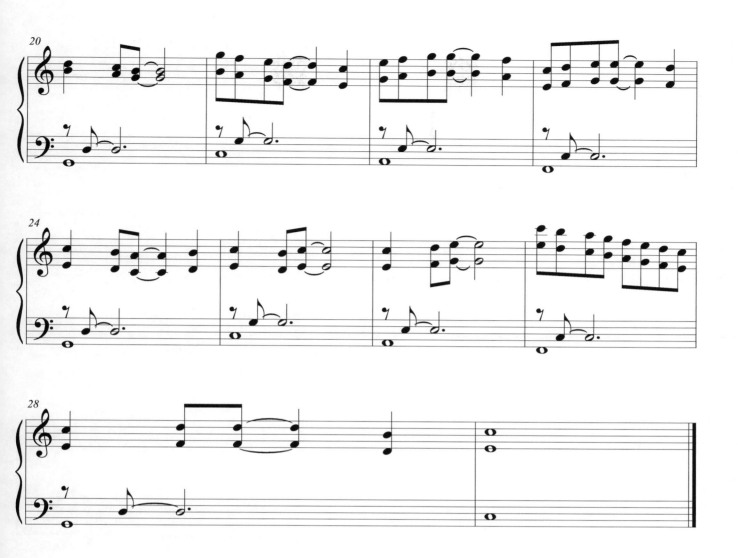

On the next page, we are going to play a simple new age piece where the left hand plays a broken 5th interval following the vi - IV - V chord progression (e.g. A minor - F Major - G Major). The right hand is primarily using only five notes - A, B, C, D, and E. Starting in measure 17, I challenge you to create a simple melody of your own using these same five notes. For fun, try playing this new age piece/exercise in every key signature.

You can simply move up in half steps through every key signature, or you can follow the cycle of 4ths (i.e. C - F - B flat - E flat, etc.) or Circle of 5ths (i.e. C - G - D - A, etc.).

Have fun trying to play this piece in every key!

Expressively (♩ = c. 108 - 120)

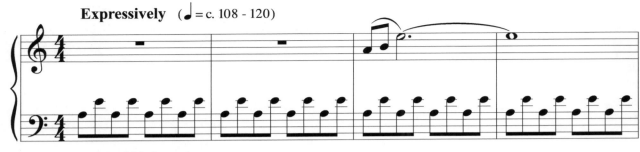

pedal ad-lib throughout

You can create your own left hand pattern starting here. Use the notes A, B, C, D, or E in any order and using any rhythm.

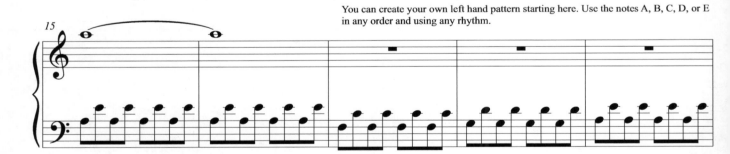

Once you feel comfortable creating a right hand melody of your own using A, B, C, D, and E, go back to the beginning of the piece and play the left hand as written but create your own melody throughout the entire new age piece.

MM00001068

On this page, we are following a I - vi - IV - V chord progression (e.g. C Major - A minor - F Major - G Major). The right hand is primarily using only 3rd intervals (e.g. C and E), and 6th intervals (e.g. E and C). Starting in measure 9, I challenge you to create a simple melody of your own using either blocked or broken 3rd or 6th intervals. For fun, try playing this new age piece/exercise in every key signature moving up in half steps.

Copyright © 2021 by Music Motivation® - http://musicmotivation.com

In the piece below, I wanted to create a simple new age sounding piece that used a perfect fifth interval with the left hand while the right hand primarily plays blocked 3rd and 6th intervals. Try it!

Morning Star

By Jerald Simon

MM00001068

In the next exercise on the next page, we are playing all blocked 3rd inverals (i.e. C and E) moving up according to the C Major scale (i.e. C D E F G A B C) while the left hand plays a 1 - 5 - 8 - 5 - 1 - 5 - 9 - 8 left hand new age pattern (i.e. C - G - C - G - C - G - D - C). After playing the third intervals, we invert the interval with the right hand - essentially we take the bottom note and move it to the top. So the third interval of C and E, for example, become E and C where C is on the top. This is known as a 6th interval. All third intervals when inverted become 6th intervals. Try playing this exercise. For fun, try to play this example in every key signature on the piano - C, C♯, D, E♭, E, F, F♯, G, A♭, A, B♭, and B.

MM00001068

In this exercise, the left hand plays a 1 - 5 - 8 - 5 - 1 - 5 - 8 - 5 left hand new age pattern (i.e. C - G - C - G - C - G - C - G) while the right hand plays 3rd and 6th intervals. Try playing this exercise. For fun, try to play this example in every key signature on the piano - C, C♯, D, E♭, E, F, F♯, G, A♭, A, B♭, and B.

MM00001068

Create a right hand melody of your own using the third and sixth intervals (blocked or broken) or any melody line you want!

Here is a simple new age piece I composed to help students learn how to combine a 1 - 5 - 8 - 5 left hand pattern with the pentascales (i.e. A minor pentascale - A, B, C, D, and E), and 3rd and 6th intervals with the right hand. In this piece, we follow a simple chord progression. We start with two measures of the A minor chord followed by one measure of the F Major chord and one measure of the G Major chord. Have fun playing this and see if you can pick out the 3rd and 6th intervals with the right hand (blocked and broken).

THE SANDS OF TIME

You can watch the music video of this New Age piece on my YouTube channel at this link: https://tinyurl.com/thesandsoftimebyJeraldSimon

BY JERALD SIMON

MM00001068

MM00001068

Now it's your turn. In the example below, follow the 1 - 5 - 8 - 5 left hand pattern according to the chord progression (e.g. Am - F - C - G, or Dm - F - C - G, or F - Am - C - G). You can compose a melody of your own, using intervals or individual notes. Try to use some of the patterns and progressions from the previous pages and see if you can come up with your own new age composition following this chord progression.

You can create any melody you want with the right hand. Start by using blocked and broken 3rd and 6th intervals
Next start using the notes from each pentascale of the chord found above the Treble clef (Am, F, C, G - as an example
with the A minor chord - use A, B, C, D, and E with the right hand, with the C major chord - use C, D, E, F, and G, etc.).

Here is a simple new age piece I composed to help students learn how to combine 4th and 5th intervals with the left hand while the right hand primarily plays the notes between a 6th interval.

Smooth Sailing

By Jerald Simon

MM00001068

Here is a simple new age piece I composed to help you see the practical application of everything we have talked about so far in this book. Notice how the left hand begins with a 1 - 5 - 8 - 5 left hand pattern (e.g. C - G - C - G), and how this piece follows a chord progression of C - C - Am - Am - F - F - G. The right hand is playing a simple melody and uses primarily 6th intervals.

NEW WORLD EXPEDITION

BY JERALD SIMON

Gently and with Feeling ♩ = 70

Students add their own dynamics.

MM00001068

Here is a simple new age pattern known as the 1 - 5 - 8 - 9 - 10 left hand pattern (e.g. C - G - C - D - E). The right hand is playing a 3rd and 6th intervals.

pedal ad-lib throughout

Here is a simple new age pattern known as the 1 - 5 - 8 - 9 - 10 left hand pattern (e.g. C - G - C - D - E). The right hand is playing a 3rd and 6th intervals.

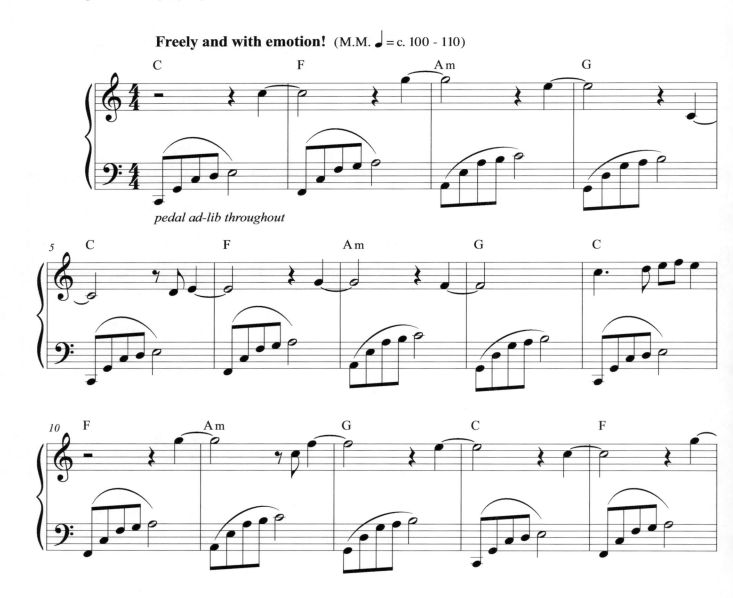

MM00001068

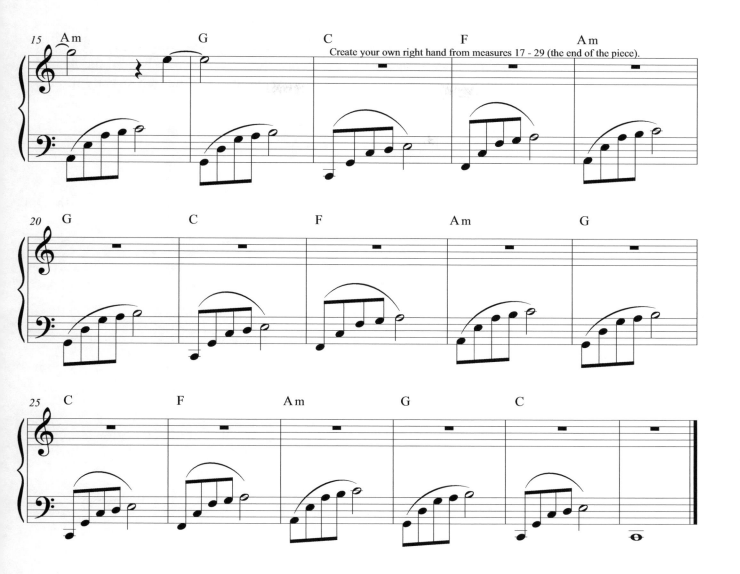

Create your own right hand from measures 17 - 29 (the end of the piece).

Here is a simple new age pattern known as the 1 - 5 - 8 - 9 - 10 left hand pattern (e.g. C - G - C - D - E). The right hand is playing 3rd and 6th intervals. For fun, try to play this example in every key signature on the piano - C, C♯, D, E♭, E, F, F♯, G, A♭, A, B♭, and B.

pedal ad-lib throughout

Here is a simple new age piece I composed to help you see the practical application of the 1 - 5 - 8 - 9 - 10 left hand pattern. Have fun playing this new age piece and follow the dynamics to bring out the feeling of the music as it crescendos and de-crescendos. This is to be played with feeling, but sweetly (dolce) and tenderly.

MEMORIES

BY JERALD SIMON

MM00001068

Have fun playing this New Age Cool song. The left hand is simply playing a 1 - 5 - 8 - 9 - 10 left hand pattern that starts on A and then moves to F, C, and ends on G. It's a simple chord progression.

Passages

BY JERALD SIMON

same fingering throughout

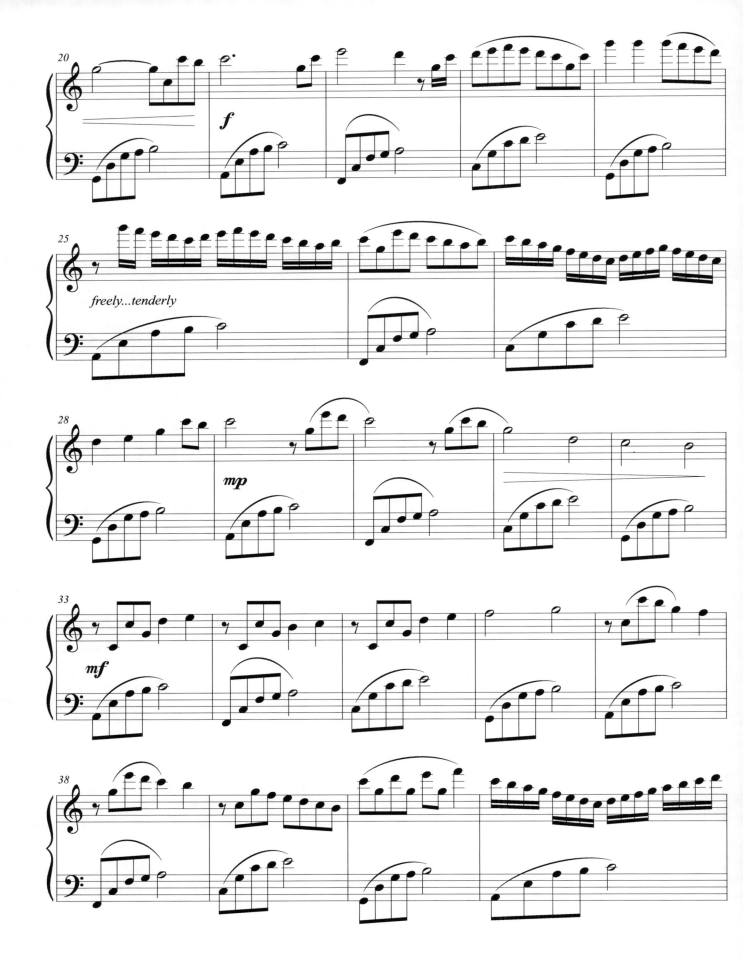

MM00001068

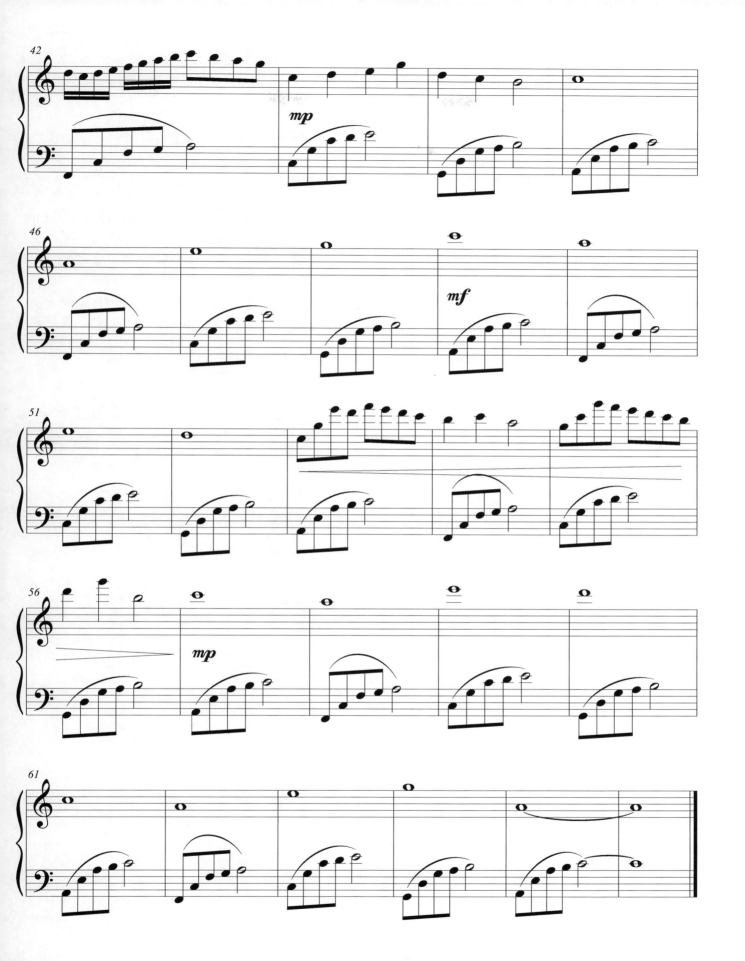

In Reflection, the left hand continues on with our 1 - 5 - 8 - 9 - 10 left hand pattern, but the right hand moves up and down several octaves on the piano.

REFLECTION

You can watch the music video of this New Age piece on my YouTube channel at this link: https://tinyurl.com/reflectionbyJeraldSimon

BY JERALD SIMON

MM00001068

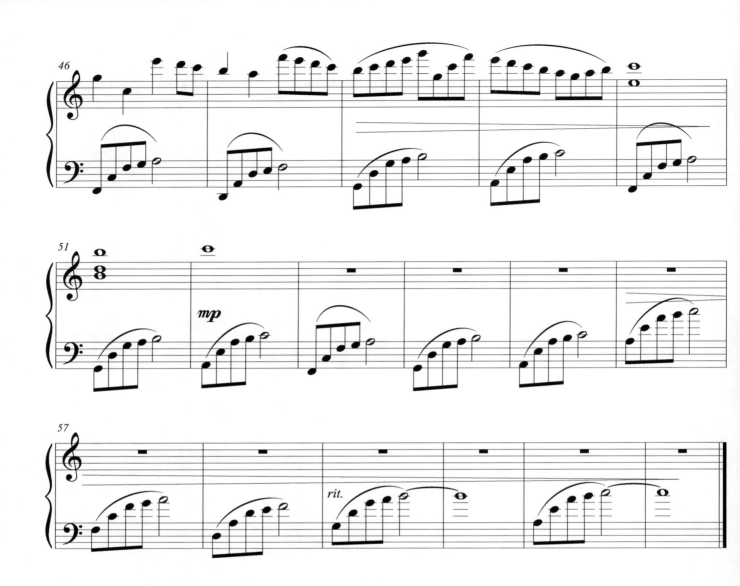

MM00001068

In this example, the left hand plays the 1 - 5 - 8 - 9 - 10 left hand pattern while the right hand plays a blocked major octave chord, followed by a broken descending 7th chord (major, minor, or diminished). We start on C and move up diatonically according to the C Major scale - C D E F G A B and C. This is a fun and simple way to start experimenting with the blocked and broken chords for both hands. Even though it is not written, try to go back down after you reach the end. Think of it as going backwards - what goes up must come down. For fun, try to play this example in every key signature on the piano - C, C♯, D, E♭, E, F, F♯, G, A♭, A, B♭, and B.

In this exercise, the left hand is playing a 1 - 5 - 8 - 5 - 9 - 5 - 10 - 5 left hand pattern. We are following a progression of Am - F - G (vi - IV - V). Starting in measure 14, you can create your own right hand melody. I have not added any dynamics to this exercise, so feel free to play this however you'd like. You can even write your own dynamics.

MM00001068

Now create your own right hand melody.
Try it! See what you can create. Follow the chord progressions.

In Song of Serenity, the left hand plays an ostinato pattern (a repetitive pattern) using the 1 - 5 - 8 - 5 left hand pattern, but the right hand moves up and down playing 6th intervals. Have fun with this!

SONG OF SERENITY

You can watch the music video of this New Age piece on my YouTube channel at this link: https://tinyurl.com/songofserenitybyJeraldSimon

BY JERALD SIMON

MM00001068

MM00001068

In this exercise, the left hand is playing a 1 - 5 - 8 - 5 - 9 - 5 - 10 - 5 left hand pattern. We are following a progression of C - F - Am - G (I - IV - vi - V). Starting in measure 19, you can create your own right hand melody. I primarily moved up and down in harmonic and melodic octave intervals. You can also use 3rd, 4th, and 6th intervals. I have not added any dynamics to this exercise, so feel free to play this however you'd like. You can even write your own dynamics. Try to play this in every key signature!

Copyright © 2021 by Music Motivation® - http://musicmotivation.com

Create your own right hand melody. You can follow the example I demonstrated from measures 1 - 18. I primarily moved up and down in harmonic (blocked) and melodic (broken) octave intervals with the right hand. You can also use harmonic or melodic 3rd, 5th, or 6th intervals as well. Try it!

MM00001068

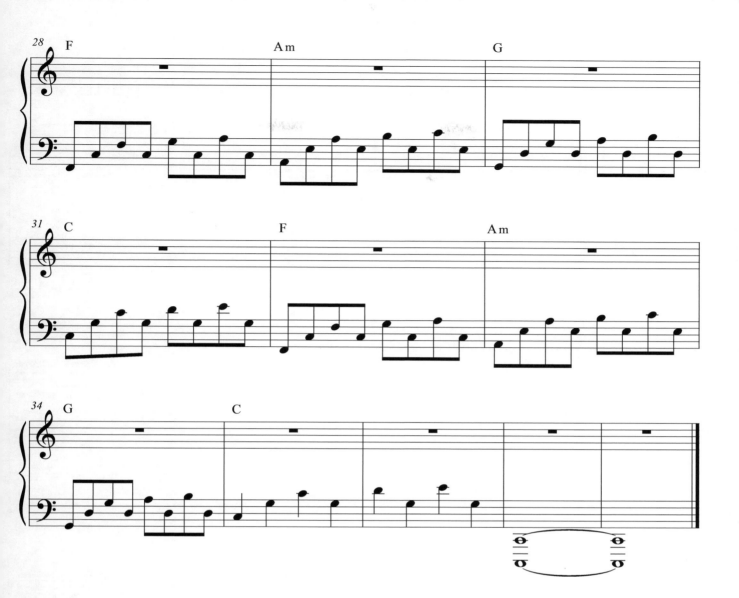

New Age-ish

with excitement (M.M. ♩ = c. 130)

BY JERALD SIMON

MM00001068

This new age piece is in 6/8 time signature. The right hand starts off primarily playing a broken D minor octave chord (e.g. D F A D up and down one octave), while the left hand plays simple triads (e.g. three note chords). Starting in measure 17 and continuing on throughout the piece, the left hand plays various new age patterns ranging from 1 - 5 - 8 to 1 - 5 - 8 - 9 - 10 and also 1 - 8 - 12 - 13 - 14 - 15. The right hand creates a simple melody using notes from the D minor scale and the D minor octave chord.

DOWNCAST

You can watch the music video of this New Age piece on my YouTube channel at this link:

BY JERALD SIMON

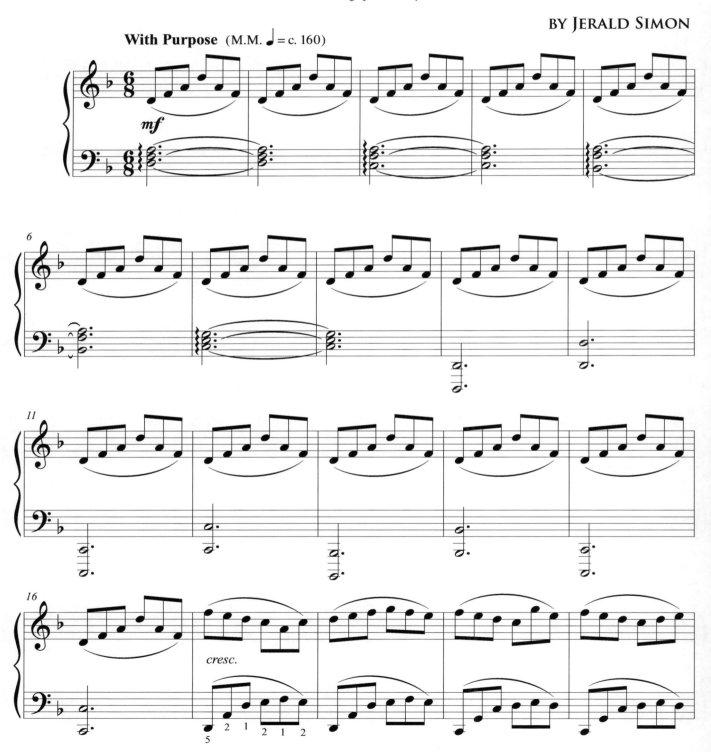

MM00001068

MM00001068

The previous two new age pieces were both written in 6/8 time signature - a common new age time signature. As you have already seen, 4/4 time signature is a common new age time signature as well. Other common new age time signatures are 3/4, 7/8, 9/8, and 12/8. Some uncommon new age time signatures are 2/2, 3/8, and 5/8 - they are still used, but not as much. You can honestly use any time signature with new age, which is a wonderful aspect of music. On this page and the following two pages, I will demonstrate how to play a similar chord progression in a new age style in 3/4, 4/4, 6/8, 7/8, 9/8 and 12/8 time signatures. The chord progression is a simple well known one - Am - F - C - G (e.g. vi - IV - I - V - in a new age style). Watch what I do to modify each hand as we change time signatures. You can try this exercise in all key signatures as well.

I won't go into too much detail in this book about all of the various new age time signatures and how you can modify the feeling and sound of a piece with the time signature. Within the Essential Piano Exercises Course, we will go more in depth in talking about common and less common key signatures in new age music. You can learn more about joining the Essential Piano Exercises Course at this link:

https://www.essentialpianoexercises.com

In this example, we are following a simple chord progression - A minor, G Major, F Major, and E minor. We are in 6/8 time signature throughout this exercise. I tried to have you play each pattern and progression with both hands. Sometimes we switch and have the right hand play what the left hand had previously played. This is a fun and simple way to start experimenting with broken chords for both hands. For fun, try to play this example in every key signature on the piano - C, C♯, D, E♭, E, F, F♯, G, A♭, A, B♭, and B.

MM00001068

In Utopia, the left hand is primarily playing octave intervals. The right hand plays various notes in a pattern using the C minor scale.

UTOPIA

You can watch the music video of this New Age piece on my YouTube channel at this link: https://tinyurl.com/utopiabyJeraldSimon

BY JERALD SIMON

MM00001068

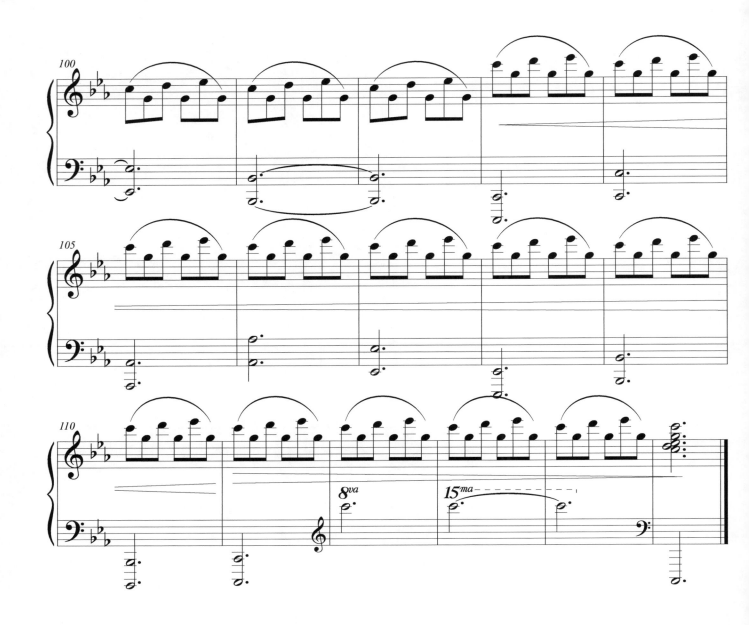

MM00001068

Let's talk about left hand New Age patterns. In my book, **"100 Left Hand Patterns Every Piano Player Should Know,"** I introduce 100 different left hand patterns from basic left hand patterns to jazz, blues, boogie, woogie, pop, rock, new age, contemporary, and classical style left hand patterns. In the book, I also include 100 songs in fake book format. The entire purpose of the book is to have students learn how to play all 100 songs from the fake book 100 different ways in every key signature. It's a great challenge and is something I did before releasing the book (the book was finished three years before I released it so I could play every song 100 different ways in every key signature - I don't challenge students and teachers to do something I have not already done myself).

There are many more left hand patterns I did not include in the book that I would have liked to, but I only wanted to introduce 100 different ways to play the same song.

When we are learning left hand patterns, we are essentially focusing on the numbers or degrees of the scale. For example, C - D - E - F - G - A - B - C are the individual notes from the C Major Scale. If we assigned numbers to each of these notes, we would start with 1 for C and continue on until we ended with 8 for the second C above the first one (e.g. C - D - E - F - G - A - B - C = 1 - 2 - 3 - 4 - 5 - 6 - 7 - 8).

If, for example, I wanted to play a left hand pattern where I rotated back and forth between the C (1) and the G (5), I could say that I am playing a 1 - 5 - 1 - 5 - 1 - 5 - 1 - 5 left hand pattern. If we were in 4/4 time signature, I would play these as 8th notes rocking back and forth from one to the other (C - G - C - G - C - G - C - G).

We can create various left hand patterns to help us play in a different style. This is what my 100 left hand patterns book is all about.

Here is an example from the book:

This pattern is a 1 - 5 - 8 - 5 - 8 - 5 - 8 - 5 left hand pattern (i.e. C - G - C - G - C - G - C - G)

If you notice in the pattern above, we are playing a basic new age pattern that I have already demonstrated at various times in this book so far. Several new age pieces have been composed using this simple left hand pattern.

It's fun to learn various left hand patterns and how to create them so you can arrange, improvise, or even compose music of your own in various styles.

On the next two pages, I have included a few patterns from my book, "100 Left Hand Patterns Every Piano Player Should Know." I only included patterns 61 - 72 from the book. There are more patterns in the book. I have included the fingering and explained what patterns you are using which were created from the major scale. Once you have learned these in the key of C, try to play each of them in every key signature moving up in half steps! Have fun with these!

New Age and Contemporary Left Hand Patterns

Once you can play these as written, then play them in all keys (simply take the pattern up half a step through every key signature)! Go on, try it!

This pattern is a 1 - 5 - 8 - 5 - 8 - 5 - 8 - 5 left hand pattern (i.e. C - G - C - G - C - G - C - G)

This pattern is a 1 - 5 - 8 - 9 - 10 - 12 left hand pattern (i.e. C - G - C - D - E - G)

This pattern is a 1 - 5 - 8 - 9 - flat the 10 left hand pattern (i.e. C - G - C - D - E-flat)

This pattern is a 1 - 5 - 8 - 9 - flat the 10 - 12 - flat the 10 - 9 left hand pattern (i.e. C - G - C - D - E flat - G E-flat - D)

This pattern is a 1 - 5 - 8 - 5 - 9 - 5 - 10 - 5 left hand pattern (i.e. C - G - C - G - D - G - E - G)

This pattern is a 1 - 5 - 8 - 5 - 9 - 5 - flat the 10 - 5 left hand pattern (i.e. C - G - C - G - D - G - E-flat - G)

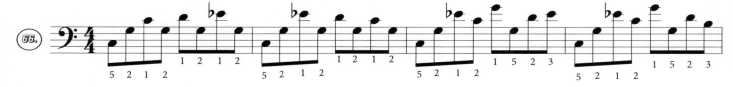

MM00001068

New Age and Contemporary Left hand Patterns

Once you can play these as written, then play them in all keys (simply take the pattern up half a step through every key signature)! Go on, try it!

This is a 1 - 8 - 10 - 12 - 15 left hand pattern (i.e. C - C - E - G - C)

This is a 1 - 8 - 10 - 12 - 10 - 8 - 5 - 8 left hand pattern (i.e. C - C - E - G - E - C - G - C)

This is a C Major pentascale (the first five notes of the C Major scale - i.e. C - D - E - F - G - followed by the C minor pentascale).

The C Major pentascale: C - D - E - F - G   The C Minor pentascale: C - D - E-flat - F - G

This is a variation on the notes from the C Minor Pentascale (i.e. - C - D - E-flat - F - G)

This is another variation on the notes from the C Minor Pentascale (i.e. - C - D - E-flat - F - G)

Here we play a C octave interval followed by the C Major Chord (in first inversion), then the D minor Chord (in first inversion) and concluding with the G Major Chord (in second inversion). We play this as quarter notes and then eighth notes.

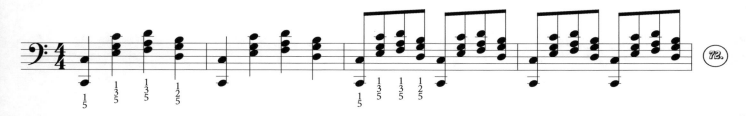

In this exercise, we are essentially playing broken triads (or three note chords) with the left hand. We follow a chord progression of Cm - Cm - Eb - Eb - Ab - Ab - G - G - Cm Cm and repeat. The left hand is simply breaking these chords apart while the right hand starts off playing a C minor scale moving up and down from measures 1 - 8. In measure 9, we play a descending C minor scale played as 8th notes. Starting in measure 17, we take the notes from the C minor pentascale (e.g. C, D, E flat, F, and G) and play it moving in thirds (e.g. C to E flat and then D to F, etc.). Starting in measure 25, you are given the freedom to be creative and come up with your own right hand melody. Create something unique and original. I have composed a new age piano solo on pages 94 - 97 that follows this progression, and the melody I created was done so by simply playing around with the C minor scale.

MM00001068

This is where you can create your own right hand melody using the notes from the C minor scale.
You can start with the C minor pentascale (C, D, E flat, F, and G)

Have fun!

The Dawn of a New Age uses a 1 - 3 - 5 left hand pattern. We are essentially playing a broken three note chord or triad. See if you can determine the chords used in each measure. It's a simple chord progression. The right hand is generally moving up and down according to the C minor scale.

THE DAWN OF A NEW AGE

You can watch the music video of this New Age piece on my YouTube channel at this link: https://tinyurl.com/thedawnofanewage

BY JERALD SIMON

MM00001068

In this exercise, we are in the key of A flat major using a 6/8 time signature and we follow a simple chord progression - A flat - F minor - D flat - E flat. The left hand pattern is a 1 - 5 - 8 - 9 - 10 - 12 left hand pattern that starts on A flat and then moves to F, D flat, and E flat. I didn't write anything in the first four measures so you can focus in learning the left hand which is repeated throughout the exercise. Starting in measure five, the right hand plays an A flat major pentascale (e.g. A flat, B flat, C, D flat, and E flat). We ascend up and then go down the pentascale. Starting in measure 13 I take the chords from the chord progression and break them apart. We begin doing octave major chords that are blocked (measures 17 - 20) and broken (measures 21 - 24). Starting in measure 25 you can create your own melody. I have composed a new age piano solo on pages 100 - 102 that follows this progression.

This is where you can create your own right hand melody using the notes from the A flat major scale.
You can start with the A flat major pentascale (A flat, B flat, C, D flat, and E flat).

Copyright © 2021 by Music Motivation® - http://musicmotivation.com

Heaven on Earth is in 6/8 time signature and is in the key of A flat major. The left hand primarily plays a 1 - 5 - 8 - 9 - 10 - 12 left hand pattern throughout the piece. Have fun playing this!

Heaven on Earth

You can watch the music video of this New Age piece on my YouTube channel at this link: tinyurl.com/heavenonearthbyJeraldsimon

By Jerald Simon

MM00001068

MM00001068

On this page and pages 104 - 105, I include over 100 measures of right hand improvisational patterns you can use to create and compose new age music of your own. We are in the key of C for these. I have only used 4/4 and 6/8 time signatures, but you can adapt these any way you want.

These are all new age fills and improvisational patterns you can use to compose new age music of your own. Each line is unique and can be used on its' own. You can mix and match and combine these in any order.

The left hand can play any left hand pattern you want from this book. You can start on C and do 1 - 5 - 8 - 1 or start on A.

You can use any of these right hand new age fills or patterns with any left hand chords or patterns you'd like to play!

Each measure is also it's own individual new age fill and can be combined with any left hand pattern in any order.

Mix and match and see what you can come up with on your own. Improvise, arrange, and compose new age music!

Copyright © 2021 by Music Motivation® - http://musicmotivation.com

105

Hereafter is in 6/8 time signature and is in the key of E flat major - though the piece is played in the relative minor key signature of C minor. The left hand begins with broken triads and moves to a 1 - 5 - 8 - 5 - 8 - 5 pattern as well as a 1 - 5 - 8 - 10 - 12 - 15 left hand pattern. Have fun playing this!

Hereafter

You can watch the music video of this New Age piece on my YouTube channel at this link: https://tinyurl.com/hereafterbyJeraldSimon

By Jerald Simon

MM00001068

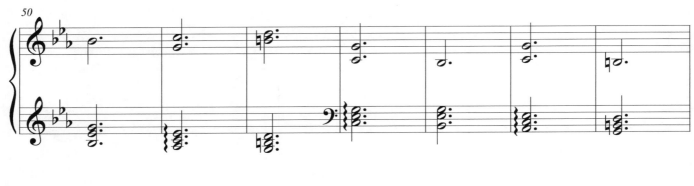

MM00001068

In this exercise, we will try to take simple chords (e.g. C6, Cm6, Csus4, etc.) and try to create a melody using the notes from the chords. This is a fun exercise to practice. You can do this with any chord from any key signature. Essentially we are taking the notes from the chord and creating a melody. This will help you as you compose a new age melody of your own. When you first begin trying this, follow the examples I have given below. Once you feel comfortable with the examples I have provided, try to create a different melody using the same notes from the chords below. It is a fun skill to develop. Essentially we are learning how to compose a melody. Every musical song, piano solo, piece, etc., needs a melody and harmony. We are learning how to develop melodies of our own on this page.

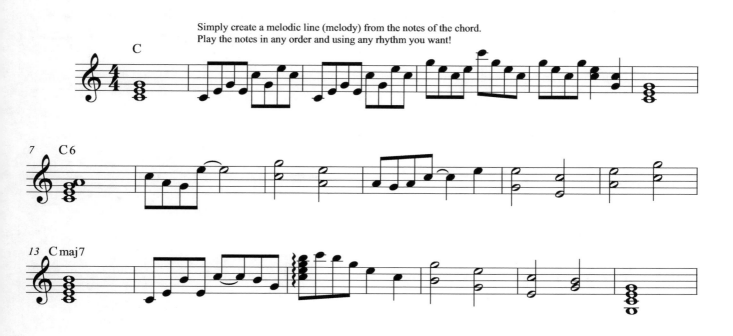

Now take the notes from a C major chord and the C major scale and see what you can create. Here is my example. Try to create/compose something like this. Make it your own melody!

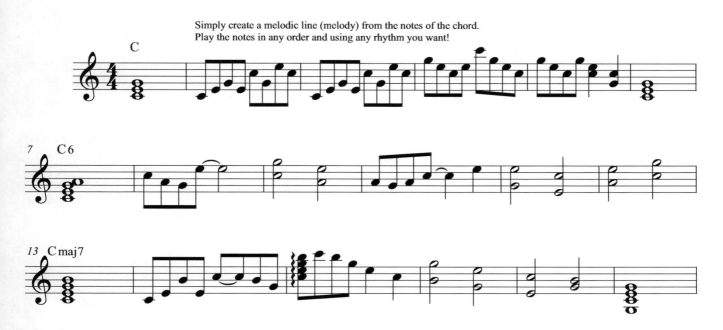

In the exercise below, the left hand is practicing a descending octave interval that more or less follows a descending C major scale. The right hand is playing a broken Cadd2 chord (3rd inversion). This is an example creating a melody by using chords. Starting in measure 24, you get to create a melody of your own. Try to take various chords and break them apart as I did. See what you can create!

MM00001068

Try to follow this progression and create a melody all your own that is in 6/8 time signature. You can follow a similar pattern of the melody I created. See what you come up with. Part of creating a melody is to create, play around, improvise, and experiment. Have fun with this!

Tranquility is in a 4/4 time signature and is in the key of C major - though the piece is played in the relative minor key signature of A minor. The left hand begins with a simple 1 - 5 - 8 left hand pattern and then plays a 1 - 5 - 8 - 5 - 7 - 5 - 8 - 5 left hand pattern and several other patterns. Have fun playing this!

TRANQUILITY

You can watch the music video of this New Age piece on my YouTube channel at this link: https://tinyurl.com/tranquilitybyJeraldSimon

BY JERALD SIMON

MM00001068

MM00001068

This is an exercise/composition that we will both compose together. I have composed the first half of the new age piano solo, and you will finish the composition by creating the last half. Chords are provided for each measure so you can follow the chord progression and I have kept a simple left hand pattern throughout the entire piece so you can focus on creating a melody for the right hand. If you get rich and famous from your half of this new age piece, remember, I should get credit for at least half of this piece!

Name this New Age piece

BY JERALD SIMON & YOU

From here until the end of the exercise, try to create your own right hand melody. Use examples from pages 103 - 105 or anything you feel like using.

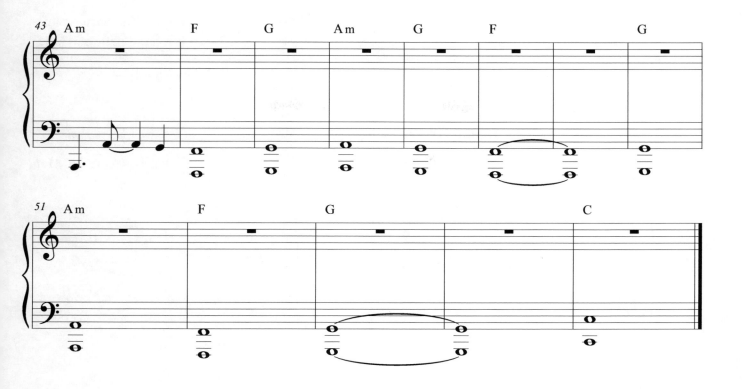

Destiny is in a 4/4 time signature and is in the key of C minor. See if you can figure out the various left hand patterns in this new age piece. The first measure uses a 1 - 8 - 12 - 15 - 16 left hand pattern. Have fun playing this!

DESTINY

You can watch the music video of this New Age piece on my YouTube channel at this link: https://tinyurl.com/destinybyJeraldSimon

BY JERALD SIMON

MM00001068

In this exercise, the left hand plays a simple 1 - 5 - 8 - 9 - 10 left hand pattern following a vi - IV - G - vi chord progression (e.g. Am - F - G - Am)

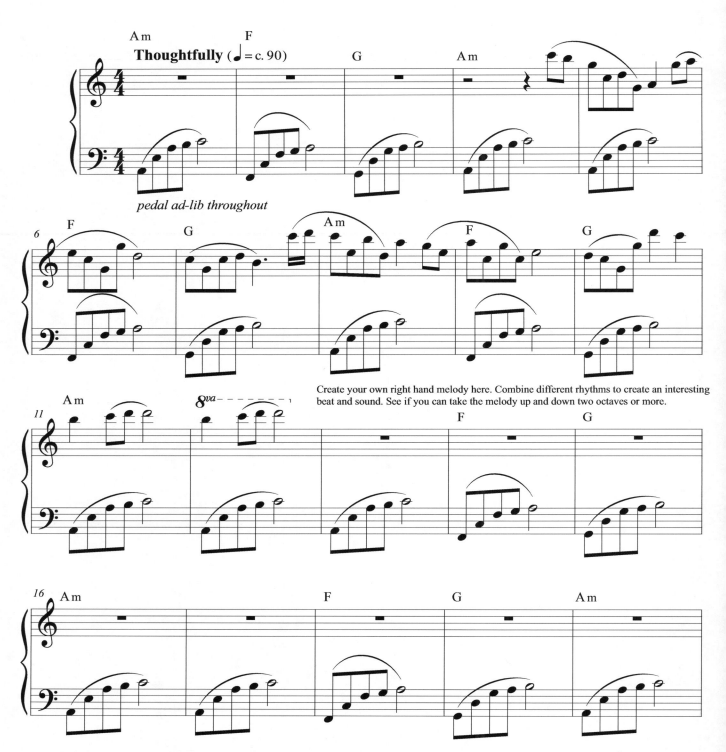

Create your own right hand melody here. Combine different rhythms to create an interesting beat and sound. See if you can take the melody up and down two octaves or more.

Throughout this exercise, I have only included the basic 1 - 5 - 8 - 9 - 10 new age left hand pattern. Think of this as a starting point. It's okay, but how many other left hand patterns from this book can you use? What can you create or come up with? How can you take some of the left hand patterns found on pages 90 - 91 and use multiple left hand patterns with this exercise? Try it! If you see an Am, F, or G, simply start on A, F, or G and follow any left hand pattern from this book to create your own unique sound. It's fun to experiment and noodle around on the piano.

MM00001068

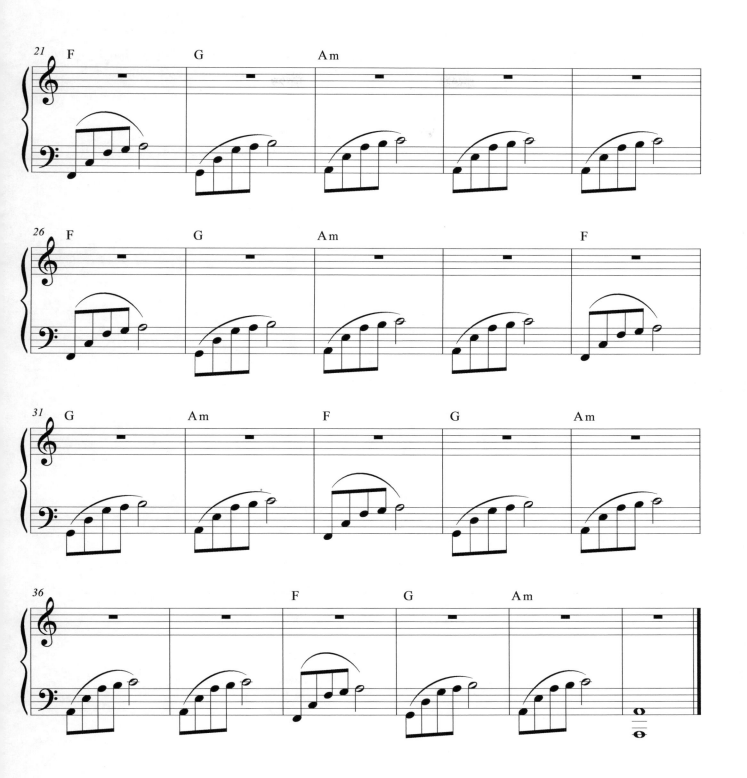

Resolution is in a 4/4 time signature and is in the key of C major. We primarily use a simple 1 - 5 - 8 - 9 - 10 left hand pattern in the beginning and then the left hand takes off on the second page. The right hand is playing several 6th and 8th (octave) intervals with a few octave chords. Have fun playing this!

RESOLUTION

You can watch the music video of this New Age piece on my YouTube channel at this link: https://tinyurl.com/resolutionbyJeraldSimon

BY JERALD SIMON

MM00001068

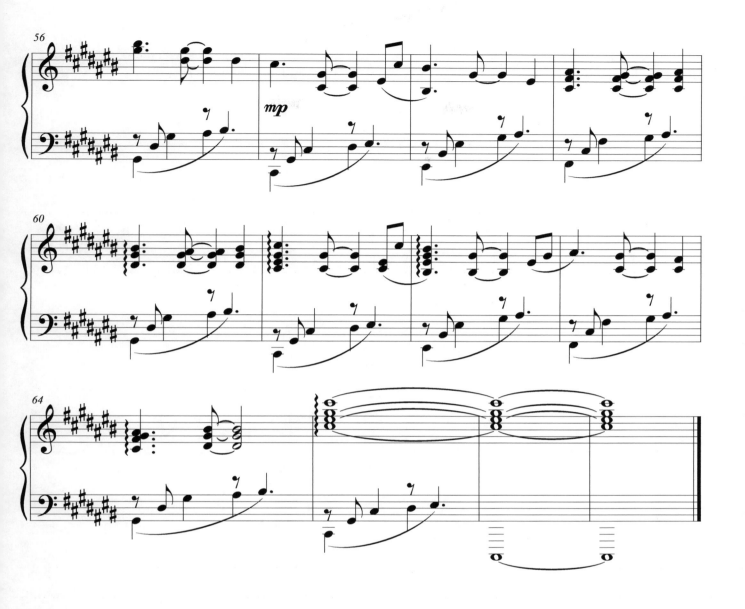

COMMOTION is in 4/4 time signature and is in the key of C minor. The left hand begins with a 1 - 5 - 8 - 9 - 10 left hand pattern and then plays octave intervals while the right hand creates a melodic line using the notes from the C minor scale. We then play octave chords and a bit of everything!

COMMOTION

You can watch the music video of this New Age piece on my YouTube channel at this link:

BY JERALD SIMON

MM00001068

Copyright © 2021 by Music Motivation® - http://musicmotivation.com

MM00001068

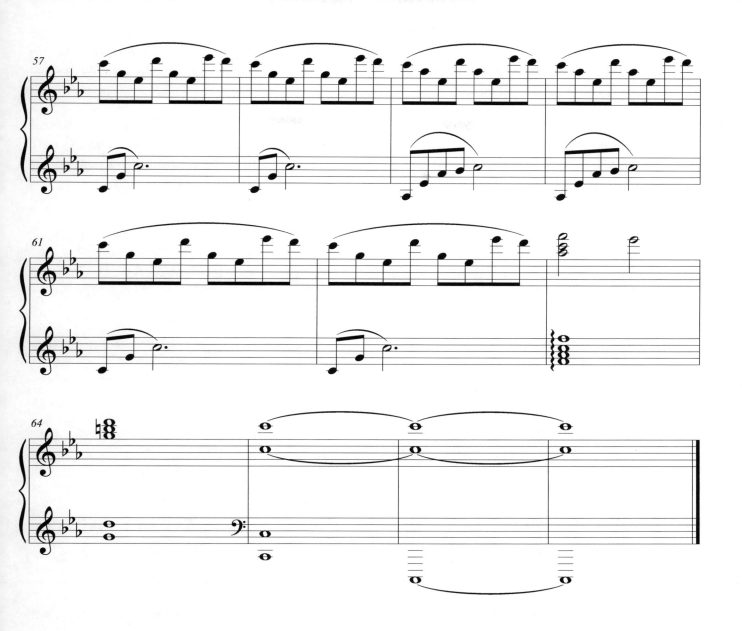

Copyright © 2021 by Music Motivation® - http://musicmotivation.com

In this exercise, we are following a familiar chord progression we have already done before. It is the vi - IV - V - vi chord progression. We are in 6/8 time signature and the left hand is simply playing the broken triads of each chord following the chord progression.

This exercise is designed to help you learn how to play 16th notes with the right hand while the left hand plays 8th notes. The next New Age piano solo, on page 134, features several 16th notes with the right hand. This is a fun exercise and, as with previous exercises, I have tried to make this sound melodious and tried to turn this into a fun exercises that sounds like an actual new age piece.

Copyright © 2021 by Music Motivation® - http://musicmotivation.com

Wintertide uses a combination of many various new age left hand patterns ranging from a simple octave to 3rd or octave to 5th interval jump to 1 - 5 - 8 - 9 - 10 and 1 - 8 - 5 - 9 - 10 - 12 - 13 patterns. You can watch the music video for this piece on my YouTube channel at this link:  https://tinyurl.com/wintertidebyJeraldSimon

WINTERTIDE

This is from the book and album also titled, "Wintertide."

BY JERALD SIMON

MM00001068

MM00001068

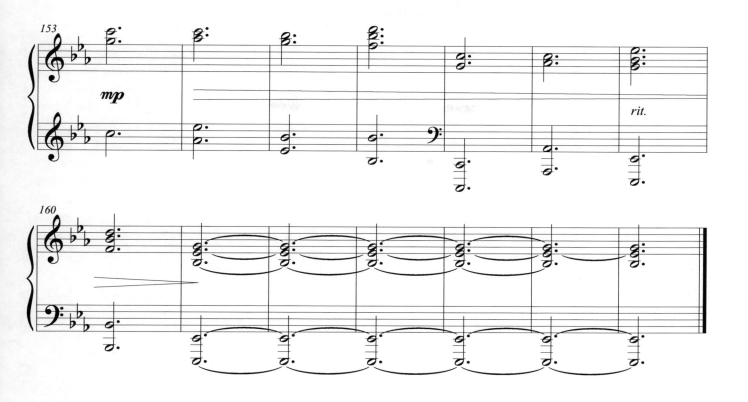

A Few Additional New Age Music Books for Piano Teachers and Parents of Piano Students

I hope you have enjoyed working through the new age piano solos and exercises in this book. I created this book primarily for all of the members of our Essential Piano Exercises Course (https://www.essentialpianoexercises.com/course). Within the course I am uploading video lessons for every exercise and piano solo from each of the current books within the series. More books are being added to the series. In addition to the videos already within the course, every member of the course has access to a weekly live piano lesson every Friday within the private Facebook group page. We have monthly themes and weekly challenges. Every live weekly piano lesson focuses on learning music theory, how to improvise, arrange, and even compose music of you own. I'd love to have you join the Essential Piano Exercises Course. After you have had a chance to play through the new age piano solos from this book, I'd love to have you film yourself playing one of my new paino solos. You can share your video of you playing my new age piano solo on social media and I'd love to have you tag me in the video (@jeraldsimon). I always enjoy watching piano students perform music I have composed and would love to see your progress as you play!

Here is a URL link to a playlist on my YouTube channel that has music videos for every new age piano solo from this book:

https://tinyurl.com/NewAgemusicvideosbyJeraldSimon

If you enjoyed these new age exercises and new age piano solos, I think you will enjoy the following!

Here are some titles to other new age music books and albums I have composed that you may enjoy:

Wintertide - https://tinyurl.com/WintertidevideosbyJeraldSimon
Sweet Melancholy - https://tinyurl.com/sweetmelancholybyJeraldSimon
Sea Fever -
Triumphant - https://tinyurl.com/TriumphantbyJeraldSimon
Sand Castles -
Castles in the Sky - https://tinyurl.com/castlesintheskybyJeraldSimon
Hymns of Exaltation - https://tinyurl.com/hymnarrangementsbyJeraldSimon

Every few months I try to release a new album/music book featuring meditation or relaxation music - all of which fall under the new age style of music. Most of these albums and books feature fully orchestrated pieces and not just piano solos. Some feature nature sounds, ocean waves, waterfalls, the wind, crickets, or other soothing nature sounds and effects that have been combined with music. Many of these compositions are meditation/relaxation because they have been composed with the intention of heping the listener be comforted, calmed, and hopefully bring peace and positivity to everyone who hear them.

You can listen to my music on Spotify, Pandora, iTunes, Amazon, and of course, you can watch all of my music videos and additional piano lesson tutorials on my YouTube channel:

youtube.com/jeraldsimon

MM00001068

A Few Additional Ideas for Piano Teachers and Parents of Piano Students

You can visit this link to read the original blog post from which this presentation was created: (https://musicmotivation.com/dont-teach-music-theory-unless-you-teach-the-practical-application/).

In the blog post I talked specifically about 10 steps to begin teaching the practical application of music theory so students know their theory inside and out. I thought I would share the 10 steps here from the blog post:

Before any piano student plays their piece, I believe they should be able to do the following (this is what I try to have my students do with their music):

1. Tell their music teacher the key signature and time signature

2. Identify all of the sharps or flats in the key signature and name them

3. Play all of the intervals created from the major key signature of the piece they are playing - this is more for piano students and possibly guitar students as many instruments only allow one note at a time. If the student is younger or new to their instrument, they can play the intervals created from the pentascales, or five note scales created from the first five notes of the major or minor scales.

4. Play through the major scale of the key signature of the piece at least 1-2 octaves up and down the piano (parallel and or contrary motion). If the student is younger or new to their instrument, as stated before, they can play the pentascales, or five note scales created from the first five notes of the major or minor scales.

5. Play or be able to play what I refer to as the "Essential Piano Exercises" from each key signature. (In the blog post I show an example from the key of C major from my book "Essential Piano Exercises" - Intervals, Scales, and Chords in all Keys and in all Inversions - a 288 page book with all intervals, scales, and simple triads and 6th and 7th chords in all keys and inversions).

These are the other 5 steps:

Once a student can do the above five essential "getting started steps" in any given key signature (and many times I will do the following steps even if they can't do the above steps in every key signature), I then challenge them to do the following five essential "music theory application steps":

1. Once the student has learned and perfected the piece, ask them to take the song up half a step and down half a step. In the beginning, this is a good start. Later on, when they are better able to do so, have them play the piece in any key signature. Start with simple pieces like "Mary Had a Little Lamb" and "Twinkle, Twinkle, Little Star." Have the students try playing these in all key signatures.

2. Ask the student to come up with at least 5-10 variations or arrangements of their piece.

3. Ask the student to compose 3-4 motifs (or single melodic line or phrase), and then put them together. This can be the beginning of creating a simple piece. I have students begin using scales and skipping notes here and there. We then have them take a simple pattern created from the notes of the major scale (1 2 3 4 5 6 7 8).

4. Ask the student to "Play a Rainbow." When I say this to students, I then begin to ask them to "play" anything. I may say: "Play me a shadow," "Play me a swing set," "Play me a thunderstorm," "Play me a puddle, a rock, a tree, a meadow, a light, etc.". The sky is the limit. I first begin with tangible objects and eventually move on to intangible ideas and concepts: "Play me loneliness," "Play me disturbed, agitated, angered, humbled, pensive, schizophrenic, etc.". Again, the sky is the limit. It is wonderful to see what students can create, even if they don't know all the rules of composition or terminology. Everyone has music within them.

5. I have students begin notating their music. I enjoy and prefer Finale, but that is because I have used it for so long and am familiar with it. There are many great programs available. After we have their music put down on paper, I then export the music from Finale as a midi file and open the midi file in Logic Pro. We then begin having them add additional instruments so they can create background tracks (this is how I create all of my weekly "**Cool Songs**" from my **COOL SONGS Series** (you can learn more about my COOL SONGS Series at this link: https://musicmotivation.com/coolsongs/). The students then have a PDF copy of their composition and an MP3 "minus track" to accompany them as they play. Talk about music motivation!

In addition, here is a link to a handout I created that I give to my own students and other piano teachers to help them learn what I call the 7 Markers of Musical Success: https://musicmotivation.com/learning-to-read-music-notation-on-the-piano/

MM00001068

Join the **Essential Piano Exercises Course** by Jerald Simon

https://www.essentialpianoexercises.com/

Gain lifetime access to the PDF books listed below (which also includes video piano lesson tutorials where Jerald Simon demonstrates examples from the books and gives piano pointers, tips to try, and the practical application of music theory where). Jerald demonstrates how to use the music theory to arrange and compose music of your own!

This course features pre-recorded video lessons so you can watch and learn how to play the piano at your convenience. You choose when and where you learn to play the piano.

Join the Essential Piano Exercises Course and receive the following PDF books along with access to weekly video lessons taught by Jerald Simon for a one time payment of $199.95.

This includes lifetime access to this course created for anyone who plays the piano!
Current books (weekly video lessons are being uploaded on these right now):
You will be able to download all of these books in PDF format...

Essential Piano Exercises Every Piano Player Should Know by Jerald Simon
100 Left Hand Patterns Every Piano Player Should Know by Jerald Simon
Essential Jazz Piano Exercises Every Piano Player Should Know by Jerald Simon
Essential New Age Piano Exercises Every Piano Player Should Know
Wintertide by Jerald Simon
Sweet Melancholy by Jerald Simon
The Dawn of a New Age by Jerald Simon
Sea Fever by Jerald Simon
Triumphant by Jerald Simon
Hymns of Exaltation by Jerald Simon
Sea Fever by Jerald Simon
Jingle Those Bells by Jerald Simon
Ghosts and Goblins and Freaks and Ghouls by Jerald Simon
Sand Castles by Jerald Simon
Platinum by Jerald Simon
I Want to Do What Jesus Taught (40 original children's primary hymns) by Jerald Simon
Jazzed about Christmas (PDF book is already available - videos coming soon)
Jazzed about 4th of July (PDF book is already available - videos coming soon)

These PDF books will be added within the course soon:

Essential Pop Piano Exercises Every Piano Player Should Know (coming in summer of 2021)
Essential Rock Piano Exercises Every Piano Player Should Know (coming in the fall of 2021)
100 Chord Progressions Every Piano Player Should Know (coming in the spring of 2022)

Join the COOL SONGS Club and start using my COOL SONGS Series...

If you would like to learn more about the COOL SONGS Series I created to help motivate and inspire piano students - especially during their teenage years, you can visit my website: https://musicmotivation.com/coolsongs.

I compose COOL SONGS to help motivate and inspire piano students!

Parents praise COOL SONGS, piano teachers rave about them, and piano students can't wait to play them! Every piano recital instantly turns into a COOL concert when students perform COOL SONGS.

There are three ways to start using the COOL SONGS I have composed and continually compose each week.

1. If you haven't already, visit this link to download my FREE COOL SONGS Starter package (12 FREE COOL SONGS with accompaniment minus tracks: http://coolsongsclub. com/freebook. There are 4 beginning level, 4 early intermediate level, and 4 intermediate - advanced level COOL SONGS) so you can start using my COOL SONGS (these are actually the same ones I have included in this book, but you will be able to download the accompaniment MP3 minus tracks and watch the video lessons as well). You will also receive my FREE 130 page PDF Book: "20 Ways to Motivate Teen Piano Students to Want to Play the Piano - the FUN WAY!"

2. If you'd like to purchase the COOL SONGS Series, you can visit this link to Purchase the entire COOL SONGS Series Course single use license (Over 4 years worth of piano lessons - 163 COOL SONGS complete with video lessons and accompaniment MP3 minus tracks) for a one time payment of $49.95: https://musicmotivation.com/coolsongs/. You'll have lifetime access to all of the COOL SONGS in the series (piano teachers will also be able to upgrade their single use license to a lifetime piano teacher studio license if they'd like to when checking out).

3. Once you have purchased the COOL SONGS Series for $49.95 and/or upgraded to a studio license if you are a piano teacher, you will then be able to join the Essential Piano Exercises Course as an added upgrade. Learn more about my **Essential Piano Exercises Course** at https://www.essentialpianoexercises.com/

Download this **FREE PDF book** -
"20 Ways to Motivate Teen Piano Students to Want to Play the Piano" at:
https://www.coolsongsclub.com/freebook.

youtube.com/jeraldsimon

I upload new videos on Mondays, Wednesdays, and Fridays on my YouTube channel, **youtube.com/jeraldsimon**. I have a few different playlists filled with great content for beginning - advanced piano students. The videos are geared for everyone from brand new piano students to music majors, professional pianists, and piano teachers of all skill levels.

There are three main playlists for my **free online piano lessons.** I offer in person piano lessons, Zoom/FaceTime piano lessons, and step by step piano lesson packages you can purchase and watch at home, but the ones listed below are FREE to everyone who subscribes to my YouTube channel:

1. # PIANO FUNdamentals (emphasis on the word FUN!)

2. # 5 Minute Piano Lessons with Jerald Simon
(sponsored by Music Motivation®)

3. # Theory Tip Tuesday Piano Lessons

I frequently release new videos. Some are piano lessons, and others are filmings of workshops, masterclasses, or concerts. I also have these additional types of videos on my YouTube channel:

a. Meditation/Relaxation Music Composed by Jerald Simon
b. Hymn Arrangements by Jerald Simon
c. Motivational Messages by Jerald Simon
d. Motivational Poetry by Jerald Simon
e. Theory Tip Tuesday (FREE Weekly Piano Lesson Videos) by Jerald Simon
f. Cool Songs by Jerald Simon (musicmotivation.com/coolsongs)
g. Assemblies, Workshops, Firesides, and more...

Let me know if you have a tutorial you'd like me to come out with to better help you learn the piano. I'm happy to help in any way I can and love hearing feedback from others about what they personally are looking for in piano lesson videos to help them learn to play the piano better. I primarily focus on music theory, improvisation/arranging, and composition. I refer to these as THEORY THERAPY, INNOVATIVE IMPROVISATION, and CREATIVE COMPOSITION.

I have also produced hundreds of COOL SONGS that teach students music theory the fun way. If you'd like to learn more about the COOL SONGS, that I composed to motivate my own piano students, or if you would like to purchase the COOL SONGS series featuring the music/books, simply visit musicmotivation.com/coolsongs to be taken to the page on my website that explains a little more about the COOL SONGS. You can also watch piano video tutorial lessons featuring 85 of the 200 + COOL SONGS (youtube.com/jeraldsimon). Let me know what you think. I'd love your feedback about the music. It helps me as I compose more COOL SONGS to motivate more piano students. I'm excited to have you watch my free video piano lessons on YouTube.com/jeraldsimon.

Perceptions, Parables, and Pointers by JERALD SIMON (read more at this link): http://musicmotivation. com/shop/motivationalself-help-books/perceptions-parables-and-pointers-by-jerald-simon/

What do you really want to do with your time? What is your mission in life? Where have you been, and where would you like to go? What are your dreams, your hopes, and your wishes? If you could do anything in the world, what would it be?

The main goal in writing down these perceptions, parables, and pointers, and in creating this book in general, is to present ideas that will help get people thinking, imagining, planning, creating, and actively participating in life.

The "As If" Principle (motivational poetry) by JERALD SIMON features 222 original motivational poems written by Simon to inspire and motivate men, women, businesses, organizations, leaders, mentors, advisers, teachers, and students. The poems were written to teach values and encourage everyone everywhere to do and be their best. (read more at this link): http://musicmotivation.com/shop/motivationalself-help-books/the-as-if-principle-by-jerald-simon/

CHECK OUT
JERALD'S
MOTIVATIONAL
BOOKS

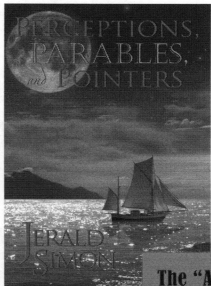

PERCEPTIONS,
PARABLES,
AND
POINTERS
$19.95

216 PAGES

A SELF-HELP
MOTIVATION
MANUAL

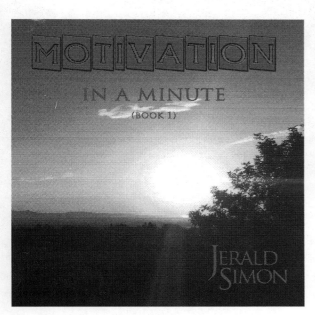

MOTIVATION IN A MINUTE
$18.95

FULL COLOR PICTURES
AND MOTIVATIONAL MESSAGES

THE "AS IF"
PRINCIPLE
(MOTIVATIONAL
POETRY)
$16.95

154 PAGES

222 INSPIRATIONAL
AND MOTIVATIONAL
POEMS WRITTEN
BY JERALD

ALL BOOKS ARE AVAILABLE ON AMAZON, BARNES AND NOBLE,
AND ALL ONLINE AND TRADITIONAL BOOK STORES

Jerald's Albums & Singles
are available from all online music stores

Stream Jerald's music on
Pandora, Spotify, iTunes, Amazon, and all streaming sites.

Check out Jerald's Cool Song Piano Packages

Jerald continually produces and releases new "Cool Songs" available for all piano students and piano teachers on his website (***musicmotivation.com***). Each new "*Cool Song*" is emailed to Music Motivation® mentees (piano teachers and piano students) who have enrolled in the "COOL SONGS" monthly subscription program. See which subscription is the best fit for you and for your piano students (if you are a piano teacher) by visiting:

http://musicmotivation.com/coolsongs

At **Music Motivation®**, I strive to produce the best quality products I can to help musicians of all ages better understand music theory (Theory Therapy), improvisation (Innovative Improvisation), and composition (Creative Composition). I try to tailor my products around the needs of piano teachers and piano students of all ages - from beginning through advanced and would love to receive your feedback about what I can do to better help you teach and learn. Let me know if there is a type of piano music, music book, fun audio or video tutorial, or any other educational product you would like to see in the field of music (principally the piano), but have not yet found, that would help you teach and learn the piano better. Please contact me. I look forward to your comments and suggestions. Thank you.

Check out these best sellers by Jerald Simon

visit *musicmotivation.com* to purchase, or visit your local music store - Chesbro music is the national distributor for all Music Motivation® books. Contact Chesbro Music Co. if you are a store (1.800.243.7276)

Learn more about
JERALD SIMON

Visit **http://musicmotivation.com/jeraldsimon**

"My purpose and mission in life is to motivate myself and others through my music and writing, to help others find their purpose and mission in life, and to teach values and encourage everyone everywhere to do and be their best." - Jerald Simon

First and foremost, Jerald is a husband to his beautiful wife, Zanny, and a father to his wonderful children. Jerald Simon is the founder of Music Motivation® (musicmotivation.com), a company he formed to provide music instruction through workshops, giving speeches and seminars, and concerts and performances in the field of music and motivation. He is a composer, author, poet, and Music Mentor/piano teacher (primarily focusing his piano teaching on music theory, improvisation, composition, and arranging). Jerald loves spending time with his wife, Zanny, and their children. In addition, he loves music, teaching, speaking, performing, playing sports, exercising, reading, writing poetry and self help books, and gardening.

Jerald created musicmotivation.com as a resource for piano teachers, piano students, and parents of piano students. In 2008 he began creating his Cool Songs to help teach music theory – the FUN way by putting FUN back into theory FUNdamentals. Jerald has also filmed hundreds of piano lesson video tutorials on his YouTube page (youtube.com/jeraldsimon). He is the author/poet of "The As If Principle" (motivational poetry), and the books "Perceptions, Parables, and Pointers", "Motivation in a Minute", and "Who Are You?". Jerald is also the author of 21 music books from the Music Motivation® Series and has also recorded and produced several albums and singles of original music.

Jerald also presents to various music schools, groups, and associations throughout the country doing various workshops, music camps, master classes, concerts and firesides to inspire and motivate teens, adults, music students and teachers. He enjoys teaching piano students about music theory, improvisation, and composition. He refers to himself as a Music Mentor and encourages music students to get motivated by music and to motivate others through music of their own.

SPECIALTIES:

Composer, Author, Poet, Music Mentor, Piano Teacher (jazz, music theory, improvisation, composition, arranging, etc.), Motivational Speaker, and life coach. Visit **http://musicmotivation.com**, to book Jerald as a speaker/performer. Visit **http://musicmotivation.com** to print off FREE piano resources for piano teachers and piano students.

Book me to speak/perform for your group or for a concert or performance:

jeraldsimon@musicmotivation.com - (801)644-0540 - musicmotivation.com

Made in the USA
Las Vegas, NV
29 January 2024

85067134R00085